Book Two

Developing Number Concepts

Addition and Subtraction

Kathy Richardson

Dale Seymour Publications®

Managing Editors: Alan MacDonell, Catherine Anderson
Developmental Editors: Harriet Slonim, Beverly Cory
Editorial Advisor: Deborah Kitchens

Production/Manufacturing Director: Janet Yearian
Production/Manufacturing Coordinator: Joan Lee
Design Director: Phyllis Aycock
Design Manager: Jeff Kelly
Text Design: Don Taka
Cover Design: Lynda Banks
Cover Illustration: Christine Benjamin
Text Illustrations: Linda Starr
Composition: Claire Flaherty

1-800-321-3106
www.pearsonlearning.com

In the years since I wrote *Developing Number Concepts Using Unifix® Cubes*, I have come to believe even more strongly in my teaching approach for ensuring children's success in mathematics. Whether it is the research on how the brain works or the new learning theories that are being refined or developed, the information we have continues to validate my belief that children need meaningful experiences that engage their thinking. We teachers are coming to a renewed appreciation of how vital our role is to the learning process. While we recognize that the child must do the learning, we also recognize that we are an important part of that learning. When we know our children well and fully understand what we are trying to teach them, we can ask questions, provide experiences, and set up situations that maximize their learning.

As we continue to grow as a profession, we teachers see that there are some things that withstand the test of time. I have found that one of these things is this approach to the teaching of mathematics to young children and how it affects the way children learn. It seemed to me to be a worthy endeavor, therefore, to work to make the information that I set forth in my first book more accessible and easier to use in this series. If you have worked with my first book, you will be familiar with many of the activities in these next books. You will see how the activities have been updated by the use of other manipulatives—in addition to Unifix Cubes—and by the grouping together of all levels of any particular activity. In these books you will find questions to guide your observations of the children at work and more help in meeting the wide variety of children's needs. And, you will find realistic classroom scenes that will help make my teaching approach come to life.

Despite these changes from my original book, the actual teaching techniques remain the same with the exception of the treatment of two topics—double-digit addition and double-digit subtraction. If you have been using my first book, you may want to take a special look at how my thinking about the best way to teach these topics has evolved. And so, I hope that if you are one of the many teachers who found your teaching to be helped by the old "Brown Book" (as some have called it) you will find this new series to be even more helpful.

KR

Acknowledgments

No one ever writes a book alone. The words that appear on the final pages come from the myriad of experiences that an author brings to the task. There are more people than I can name who led me to and helped me through the writing of this series. To all the teachers and teacher leaders I have worked with over the years, and to all the children who let me enter their lives and learn from them, I give thanks. And to everyone in my large and wonderful family, ever patient with my preoccupation with my work, I give my gratitude and love.

There are some people who were particularly important in helping me get this project done and to whom I would like to express my appreciation. The old cliché "I couldn't have done it without you" is once again true. Special thanks to Deborah Kitchens and Janann Roodzant. The phrase "countless hours" comes to mind when I think of all the time they dedicated to helping me. And thanks to Jody Walmsley, Patti Boyle, Marilyn Smith, Kathy McGrath, and Barb Escandon—who kept me in touch with real kids and real classrooms—to Ruth Parker who continues to stretch my thinking, and to Linda Gregg—who kept me moving and wouldn't let me give up. Special thanks to Linda Starr for bringing these books to life through her delightful illustrations.

Some thoughts never dim with the passing of time. In memory of Mary Baratta-Lorton, who is always present in my work and in my heart.

Credits

Unifix® Cube is a registered trademark of Philograph Publications, Ltd.

Snap™ Cube is a trademark of the Cuisenaire® Company of America.

Baratta-Lorton, Mary (1976). *Mathematics Their Way*. Menlo Park, CA: Addison-Wesley Publishing Company, Inc.

Richardson, Kathy (1998). *How Do We Know They're Learning? Assessing Math Concepts*. Bellingham, WA: Lummi Bay Publishing Co.

Richardson, Kathy (1990). *A Look at Children's Thinking*. (Video II) *Assessment Techniques: Number Combinations and Place Value*. Norman, OK: Educational Enrichment, Inc.

D'Nealian® Handwriting is a registered trademark of Donald Neal Thurber. Used by permission of Addison Wesley Educational Publishers, Inc.

Introduction

CHAPTER ONE: Interpreting and Symbolizing Addition and Subtraction, *p. 1*

Teacher-Directed Activities

Independent Activities

CHAPTER TWO: Internalizing Number Combinations to 10, *p. 41*

    A Classroom Scene, *p. 48*

    About the Activities, *p. 54*

CHAPTER THREE: Developing Strategies for Adding and Subtracting, *p. 99*

    A Classroom Scene, *p. 104*

    About the Activities, *p. 111*

The blackline masters numbered for use with this book are listed below. (For a complete listing of the blackline masters used in the *Developing Number Concepts* series see pages 173–174.)

Developing Number Concepts—the Series

Developing Number Concepts is a series of books designed to help young children develop important foundational mathematics concepts.

Each of the three books in the series includes cohesive and organized sets of experiences focused on particular mathematical ideas. Every concept is developed both through teacher-directed and independent activities. Because children learn at different rates the activities are "expandable" and, therefore, meet a range of needs. Questions that guide teachers' observations of children as they work and learn help in the assessment of children's ongoing progress.

Book One

Chapter 1: *Beginning Number Concepts*
Chapter 2: *Pattern*
Chapter 3: *The Concepts of More and Less*

Book Two

Chapter 1: *Interpreting and Symbolizing Addition and Subtraction*
Chapter 2: *Internalizing Number Combinations to 10*
Chapter 3: *Developing Strategies for Adding and Subtracting*

Book Three

Chapter 1: *Place Value*
Chapter 2: *Beginning Multiplication*
Chapter 3: *Beginning Division*

The Planning Guide for Developing Number Concepts accompanies the series. It is for the use of teachers of kindergarten through grade three and teachers of multigrade classes. It includes comprehensive year-long teaching plans along with classroom management ideas.

Each chapter of *Books One, Two,* and *Three* includes the following.

■ What You Need to Know About...

This section provides the teacher with background information on the featured math concept and a summary of ways in which to teach the concept.

■ Chapter Overview

A brief overview of the chapter follows. It offers pertinent information on how the math concept should be taught to children at each grade level, kindergarten through grade three, and to children with special needs.

■ Goals for Children's Learning

This section lists the mathematics concepts, ideas, and skills that the children will learn as they work with the activities.

■ Analyzing and Assessing Children's Needs

Questions to guide teachers' observations and a discussion of how the activities can be used to meet a range of needs are included. The questions are geared to help teachers determine if the tasks that children are working with are appropriate and are meeting their needs.

■ Classroom Scenes

Realistic classroom scenes that deal with the major math concepts covered in the chapter help bring the activities to life as they model ways in which the teacher can work.

■ About the Activities

Included here is a brief discussion about the purpose of the activities along with information about materials preparation.

■ Teacher-Directed Activities and Independent Activities

A great variety of both teacher-directed and independent and/or partner activities are included for each math concept. This gives teachers many different ways to meet children's needs while it gives children many different ways to learn about a particular concept.

■ Blackline Masters

Blackline masters, used both for materials preparation and as children's worksheets, appear at the end of each book.

Children's first experiences with numbers will influence the way they deal with mathematics for the rest of their lives. Children will benefit from and will be able to build on their early experiences if they learn mathematics in ways that make sense to them. These books are for teachers who want to make mathematics understandable to children and who want to help children build a mathematics foundation that will serve them in the years to come.

Guiding Principles

The approach presented here is based on certain principles of how children learn. It will be most effective if presented in light of these principles, some of which follow.

Children develop an understanding of concepts through experiences with real things rather than symbols. Teachers and parents have known for generations that children learn from real-life experiences. Such wisdom grew from observing children over time. It has been validated by the latest research on how the brain works and by current educational theories on how children learn. The activities presented in this series engage children in exploring, discovering, and interacting with mathematical concepts in ways that get them to think critically. The approach goes even further as it offers a wealth of activities that provide children with ongoing practice that will enable them to develop facility and fluency with mathematical ideas. In the past, children may have practiced number concepts by working solely with workbook exercises. The activities in *Developing Number Concepts* provide the practice children need but in ways that are more engaging and meaningful.

Teachers can support the development of understanding by presenting planned and focused experiences and by interacting with the children as they work. Children must come to their own understanding of the concepts and gain competence and facility for themselves. Teachers play an important role in supporting concept development by planning mathematical experiences for children that help them confront, interact with, and practice particular mathematical ideas. When teachers have children work with sets of related activities that meet a range of needs, they can observe all the children at work and then interact with them individually in ways that enhance children's learning.

For children to be engaged by a particular mathematical task, they need to be on the edge of their understanding or level of competence. Children will find tasks engaging if the experiences meet their needs for developing new understandings or for developing confidence or competence with a new skill. Developing competence is a prime motivator for young children. They will naturally choose to practice a seemingly simple task over and over again until they no longer find it challenging.

When working independently, children should be allowed to choose from a group of related tasks. Children do not all work and learn at the same pace. They do not all stay interested and focused for the same amounts of time. When teachers provide children with a choice of tasks, they can each select the one they think is the most interesting and valuable. They are more likely to be productively engaged when they are in control of—and are, therefore, responsible for—having made that particular choice. Children should be free to choose to do any particular task over and over again. They get the most from a task when they are free to come back to it as many times as they think is necessary.

The most powerful learning experiences have value in being repeated. Many enthusiastic teachers believe that in order to provide the best math program possible, they must continually present new and different activities. However, this may not be the best way for children to develop an understanding of the concepts that are the most important for them to learn. Learning how to do an activity is just the beginning. Not until children fully understand how to do a task are they ready to learn from it. When children are encouraged to work with familiar tasks over time, they will get the full benefit from the experience. The teachers' focus can then shift from making sure the children know what to do to using the experience to help children deepen conceptual understandings.

In order for number concepts to be meaningful to them, children must experience numbers as they occur in the real world. Children need to count, compare, combine, and take apart numbers using a variety of manipulatives. Their work with manipulatives helps them discover mathematical relationships and build visual images. There are many different manipulatives that can be used as effective models of mathematical ideas and relationships. Some of these are commercially available and others can be gathered by and/or made by teachers. The following manipulatives are suggested for use with the activities in this series. Classroom quantities of each are specified.

Connecting, or Interlocking, Cubes

Many of the activities require the use of ¾-inch connecting cubes. These manipulatives can be linked to form "trains" or "towers." Approximately 1,000–2,000 connecting cubes will be needed. They can be found under the following brand names:

> **Unifix® Cubes**
> **Snap™ Cubes**

Counters

A great many activities rely on the use of counters. A variety of manipulatives should be used as counters, thus enabling children to experience the same activity with different models. The following manipulatives can be used effectively as counters:

> **Unifix® Cubes or Snap™ Cubes** (used individually)
> **Color Tiles** (400–800)
> **Wooden Cubes** (500)
> **Collections** (15–20) Each collection should consist of 60–100 small items of one kind, such as buttons, shells, screws, pebbles, and bread tags.

Additional Manipulatives

Some activities require specific manipulatives, such as the following:

> **Toothpicks, flat** (3 or 4 boxes)
> **Pattern Blocks** (3 sets)
> **Beans** (2 lb) and portion cups, available in restaurant-supply stores (for place-value activities)

The following charts identify mathematics concepts that children need to know and understand. They also list the Book Two (2:) activities—teacher-directed and independent—that can be used to support children's learning of the concepts. Some activities meet a variety of needs and so are listed in several places. Refer to the section entitled "Questions to Guide Your Observations," in each Chapter Overview, to help you determine those needs.

Chapter 1: Interpreting and Symbolizing Addition and Subtraction

If your children need...	Teacher-Directed Activities	Independent Activities
practice interpreting (acting out) addition and subtraction stories: These experiences help children distinguish between the processes of addition and subtraction and help them understand that these processes occur in the real world. This provides a foundation for later work with symbols.	2: 1–1 Acting Out Stories: Using Real Things 2: 1–2 Acting Out Stories: Using Fantasies 2: 1–3 Acting Out Stories: Using Counters	
practice in reading and interpreting addition and subtraction equation cards and in relating each to a corresponding story or action: After acting out addition and subtraction stories, children need to associate these experiences and actions with symbolic representations.	2: 1–4 Modeling Addition and Subtraction Equations 2: 1–5 Acting Out Stories To Go with Equations, Level 1 2: 1–6 Roll and Count 2: 1–7 Listen and Count 2: 1–8 Grow and Shrink: Using the Plus (+) and Minus (−) Signs	2: 1–12 Counting Boards: Reading Equations 2: 1–13 Race to Ten 2: 1–14 Plus-and-Minus Train 2: 1–15 Clear the Deck
practice in writing addition and subtraction equations to describe problems: Children write their own equations to label situations that you have previously modeled.	2: 1–9 Writing Equations To Label Addition and Subtraction Stories, Levels 1 and 2	2: 1–16 Writing Equations with Counting Boards
practice in writing a story problem to go with an equation: Writing stories adds another dimension to interpreting equations. This provides children with a way to permanently record their ideas.	2: 1–10 Writing Stories To Go with Equations	2: 1–17 Writing Stories To Match Equations
practice in interpreting complex addition and subtraction stories: This activity gives children experiences with stories that involve missing addends and comparative subtraction.	2: 1–11 Working with Complex Addition and Subtraction Stories	

Chapter 2: Internalizing Number Combinations to 10

If your children need...	Teacher-Directed Activities	Independent Activities
practice in orally describing the parts of a number: These activities help children think about the different ways in which a number can be broken up into parts.	2: 2–1 Snap It, Level 1 2: 2–2 The Tub Game, Level 1 2: 2–3 The Wall Game 2: 2–4 Bulldozer 2: 2–5 The Cave Game, Level 1 2: 2–7 Finger Combinations 2: 2–8 Working with Number Shapes 2: 2–9 Number Shapes: On and Off 2: 2–10 Working with Number Trains 2: 2–11 Number Trains: On and Off 2: 2–12 Counting Boards: Number-Combination Stories	2: 2–14 Number Arrangements: Using Cubes, Level 1 2: 2–15 Number Arrangements: Using Color Tiles, Level 1 2: 2–16 Number Arrangements: Using Toothpicks, Level 1 2: 2–17 Number Arrangements: Using Collections, Level 1 2: 2–18 Counting Boards: Making Up Number-Combination Stories, Level 1 2: 2–19 Number-Shape Arrangements, Level 1 2: 2–20 Number Shapes: Using Number Cubes, Level 1 2: 2–22 Number-Train Arrangements, Level 1
practice in creating and describing the parts of a number using symbols to label the parts: These activities will help build facility in using symbols and will help bring meaning to the symbolic "number facts."	2: 2–13 Finding and Recording Number Combinations	2: 2–14 Number Arrangements: Using Cubes, Level 2 2: 2–15 Number Arrangements: Using Color Tiles, Level 2 2: 2–16 Number Arrangements: Using Toothpicks, Level 2 2: 2–17 Number Arrangements: Using Collections, Level 2 2: 2–18 Counting Boards: Making Up Number-Combination Stories, Level 2 2: 2–19 Number-Shape Arrangements, Level 2 2: 2–20 Number Shapes: Using Number Cubes, Level 2 2: 2–21 Number Shapes: Using Spinners 2: 2–22 Number-Train Arrangements, Level 2 2: 2–23 Number Trains: Using Number Cubes 2: 2–25 How Many Ways? 2: 2–26 Number-Train Graph 2: 2–27 Building and Rebuilding
practice in determining the missing part of a number: These activities help develop the relationships that children need to know in order to work with basic addition and subtraction facts.	2: 2–1 Snap It, Level 2 2: 2–2 The Tub Game, Level 2 2: 2–5 The Cave Game, Level 2 2: 2–6 Grab-Bag Subtraction	*(The following activities are from Chapter 3.)* 2: 3–13 Counting Boards: How Many Ways? 2: 3–15 Build-a-Floor Race, Levels 1 and 2 2: 3–22 Grab-Bag Subtraction 2: 3–25 The Snap-It Station 2: 3–26 What's Missing?

Chapter 3: Developing Strategies for Adding and Subtracting

WORKING WITH NUMBER COMBINATIONS TO 10		
If your children need...	**Teacher-Directed Activities**	**Independent Activities**
practice in solving addition and subtraction problems using numbers to 10 with increasing efficiency: These activities provide opportunities for children to move from counting to seeing relationships between quantities and developing and applying strategies.	2: 3–1 Combining Stacks: Pick It Up 2: 3–2 Instant Recognition of Number Arrangements 2: 3–3 Instant Recognition of Number Shapes 2: 3–4 Instant Recognition of Number Trains 2: 3–5 Related Combinations: Short Stacks 2: 3–6 What Do You Think? Using Counting Boards 2: 3–7 What Do You Think? Using Grab Bags 2: 3–8 What Do You Think? Using Tubs 2: 3–9 Let's Pretend: Grab Bags 2: 3–10 Let's Pretend: Counting Boards 2: 3–11 Let's Pretend: Number Trains 2: 3–12 Let's Pretend: Number Shapes	2: 3–14 Combination Toss 2: 3–15 Build-a-Floor Race 2: 3–16 Apartment Buildings 2: 3–17 Describing Shape Puzzles 2: 3–18 What Numbers Can You Make? 2: 3–19 Addition-and-Subtraction Spin-It 2: 3–20 Counting Boards: Think and Write 2: 3–21 Grab-Bag Addition 2: 3–22 Grab-Bag Subtraction 2: 3–23 Two-Color Trains 2: 3–24 The Tub-Game Station 2: 3–26 What's Missing? 2: 3–27 Comparing Combinations

WORKING WITH NUMBER COMBINATIONS TO 20		
If your children need...	**Teacher-Directed Activities**	**Independent Activities**
practice in solving addition and subtraction problems using numbers to 20 with increasing efficiency: These activities provide opportunities for children to move from counting to seeing relationships between quantities and developing and applying strategies.	2: 3–5 Related Combinations: Short Stacks 2: 3–28 Related Combinations: Tall Stacks 2: 3–29 How Do You See It? Adding Number Shapes 2: 3–30 Working with Ten-Shapes 2: 3–31 A Ten-Shape and More: Subtraction 2: 3–32 Exploring Number Relationships with the Magic Box	2: 3–33 Number-Shape Pairs 2: 3–34 Two Ten-Shapes: Addition and Subtraction 2: 3–35 A Ten-Shape and More: Subtraction Station 2: 3–36 Roll and Double 2: 3–37 Wipe Out

What You Need to Know About Addition and Subtraction

When presenting addition and subtraction to young children, it is important to recognize that meaningful learning comes from real experiences, not through work with symbols. Symbols come to have meaning only when they are associated with these real experiences.

For a very long time and continuing into the present, many people have believed that children learn to add and subtract by completing workbook pages, using flash cards, working on drill-and-practice computer programs, and taking timed tests. If children do not learn what they are expected to learn, some would say it was because they didn't have enough drill. The basic assumption underlying this belief is that children can learn what is represented by a symbol by working with the symbol itself. But this assumption does not make sense. No one believes that learning to read, write, and spell the word *chocolate* is synonymous with experiencing chocolate; but many do believe that knowing how to read and write $3 + 4 = 7$ is synonymous with understanding the number concepts represented by these symbols. However, there is nothing inherent in the symbol *3* that communicates how many objects this numeral represents.

To understand this better, put yourself in the place of a child for a moment. This exercise will help you understand what children experience when they are asked to deal with symbols before they have developed a sense of quantity. We will use the letters of the alphabet to represent the numerals. Do not automatically translate these letters into numbers and begin to think 1, 2, 3. . . because, if you do so, you will miss the insight into what children experience.

Assume $a = \bullet$　　$b = \bullet\bullet$　　$c = \bullet\bullet\bullet$　　$d = \bullet\bullet\bullet\bullet$　　$e = \bullet\bullet\bullet\bullet\bullet$ (and so forth).

Which letter belongs in each box?

　　$c + e = \square$　　$b + g = \square$　　$d + f = \square$

How did you figure out the answers? Were your fingers useful?

Now that you have figured out those answers, see how quickly you can find the answer to the following:

　　$d + e = \square$

Did you look for a relationship? Did you notice that $d + e$ had to be a less than $d + f$ because e is a less than f? Or did you revert to counting on your fingers?

Try these:

　　$e + g = \square$　　$d + b = \square$　　$g - c = \square$　　$h - e = \square$

> *Children do not gain understanding of addition and subtraction through work with symbols.*

How fast are you? What would you have to do to get faster? Could you memorize the above facts if you needed to? Would having memorized these facts be of any help in developing a sense of quantity? Would knowing the answers to addition facts help you in answering the following questions?

- How many more is *i* than *c*?
- Which is more, *c* + *f* or *b* + *h*?
- If you have *g* people at a party, would *s* cookies be enough, too many, or just about right? How many cookies would each person get?
- About how many grapes could you hold in one hand? Could you hold *h* grapes? *m* grapes?

Children who deal almost exclusively with symbols begin to feel that the symbols exist in and of themselves rather than as representations for other things. They do not connect what they know from experience to the symbols they are working with.

For example, Jackie's kindergarten teacher showed her a card with the numeral *8* written on it and said, "Show me this many with the cubes."

Jackie began to lay cubes out. Then she stopped and said, "I can't. The cubes won't make a circle." She was trying to form the shape of the numeral *8* with the cubes! It did not occur to Jackie to count out eight objects. For her, *8* was the symbol *8* and not what it represented. This is not to say that Jackie couldn't count to eight or that she couldn't get eight forks if her mother asked her to. What it does mean is that Jackie did not automatically associate the symbol *8* with the quantity of eight things.

Children can learn to be successful with symbols without fully understanding what the symbols represent, as the following examples show.

When Nora, a first-grade child, was shown the problem 5 + 4, she said, "That's nine."

The teacher said, "Show me."

Nora put out five cubes and then four more. She counted and said, "See, nine."

The teacher then said, "Show me this one," writing "8 − 3" on a small chalkboard.

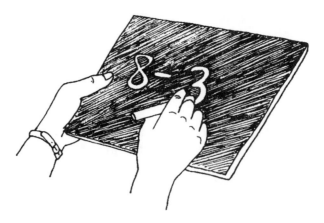

Nora said, "I know that one. That's five." She wrote the answer on the chalkboard.

The teacher again said, "Show me." So Nora put out eight cubes. She then got three more cubes and took those three cubes away.

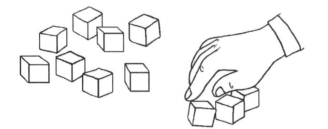

Nora looked puzzled when she saw that there were eight left instead of the five she expected, so she tried again.

To the teacher's amazement, Nora kept the three additional cubes by placing them to the left of eight cubes. She took the three cubes away again.

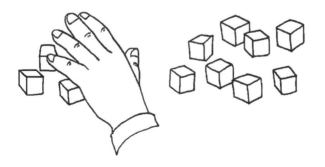

When Nora realized that she still ended up with eight cubes, she said, "I guess eight take away three is eight." She erased the 5 and wrote 8 as the answer to the problem.

Nora had learned to add and subtract with symbols, but when she was asked to demonstrate what the symbols meant, she showed that she did not really understand subtraction. Even though Nora had memorized answers to subtraction problems, she still needed to experience subtraction by acting out real situations. She needed to learn to label the experiences with the appropriate symbols until she could connect the symbols in her mind to what they represent.

Gilbert, also in first grade, was extremely proud of the fact that he knew his "pluses." His mother had bought a set of addition flash cards and she had worked with him faithfully until he knew all the facts.

One day, the teacher was working with Gilbert. She put four cubes on the table and covered them with an overturned margarine tub. When asked how many cubes were under the tub, Gilbert answered, "Four." The teacher then showed Gilbert three more cubes and placed them under the margarine tub with the other four. He knew that she had added three more cubes to the first four, but he could not see the cubes under the tub. The teacher asked, "How many cubes are under the tub now? Gilbert hesitated and then began to count on his fingers to figure it out. If the teacher had shown him the flash card 4 + 3, he could have answered "seven" without hesitation; however, when confronted by the same situation represented by real objects, he could not name the sum.

Some children know more than their work with symbols indicates. Tomás was working on the problem 1 + 8. He put out one object. Then, in attempting to count out eight more, he miscounted and actually put out seven. He then counted all the objects and arrived at eight. Without any hesitation at all, he wrote 8 as the answer to 1 + 8. Tomás had gone through a ritual for determining answers to addition problems. Then he got an answer and wrote it down.

The teacher then asked Tomás, "If you had one apple and you got eight more apples, would you have eight apples altogether?"

Tomás laughed and said, "Oh no, I would have nine apples."

Tomás knew something about number in the real world, but he did not use what he knew when solving a written problem. He did not even notice the inconsistency. The activity he was required to do at school using numerical symbols was unrelated in his mind to what he knew about numbers in the real world.

For children to clearly understand addition and subtraction, they must be able to see the connection between these processes and the world they live in. Children need to know that adding is putting groups together to determine how many and that subtracting is taking something away from a group to determine what is left (or comparing two groups to determine the difference between them). Children need to learn that certain words such as *add, subtract, total, sum, difference,* and *equals* are used to describe familiar occurrences in their everyday lives. They need to see that symbols are used as tools for keeping track of the numbers in the problems.

Children gain understanding of addition and subtraction through real-world experiences.

The number relationships that children need to understand can only be learned through counting and comparing actual groups of objects. The fact that three and four add up to seven needs to be experienced until the child knows that particular relationship. Just learning to say "three plus four equals seven" does not guarantee that the child really knows the underlying relationships implied by those words.

Compare memorizing this . . .   to working with this . . .

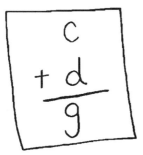

and this . . . .

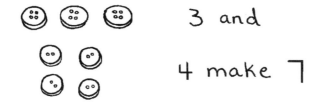

A very important task for young children in school is learning how to write things down. In mathematics class, this means that children must read and write the equations that describe the processes they are working with. The connection between the experience and the symbol is critical. As long as children separate them and deal with them as two different things, they will have trouble using symbols appropriately.

Children need to connect their experiences with the symbols used to represent those experiences.

In this technological age, when children need to learn more and different mathematics than ever before, it is important to consider where beginning addition and subtraction and the learning of basic facts fit into the bigger picture. Children need to learn mathematics so that they can solve problems of all kinds. Calculators and computers are tools that will help children do this more efficiently, but these tools can't do children's thinking for them. To use technology effectively, children need to know *more* mathematics, not less. Understanding the processes of addition and subtraction and being able to understand, interpret, and think with numbers is critical.

Children learn to add and subtract in order to solve problems.

Children must be able to deal with two aspects of solving problems. First, they must be able to interpret problems correctly. That is, they need to know what the problem is asking. Then, they must have facility with whatever numbers they need to use to solve the problem. If we want children who are effective problem solvers, then we must recognize the importance of these two aspects and help children to develop competence in both.

What we will deal with in this book are ways to most effectively build the foundation that our children need to work successfully with the more complex problems they will encounter.

Teaching and Learning Addition and Subtraction

It is important that children's early work with addition and subtraction be meaningful in order to prepare them for solving problems with confidence and efficiency. The activities in this book help children see addition and subtraction as processes that occur in the real world. Through their work with the activities, children develop a strong sense of quantity, number combinations, and number relationships. Symbols are introduced as tools for recording children's experiences with these processes and relationships.

The activities are organized into three chapters, each dealing with important concepts that children must internalize if they are to be successful with the increasingly complex problems they will work with throughout their school years. All three chapters offer both teacher-directed and independent activities to support the development of these concepts.

Chapter 1: Interpreting and Symbolizing Addition and Subtraction

Addition and subtraction are introduced through story problems. Children act out the problems in various ways and learn to record their actions with conventional symbols. Also included are activities that focus on the difference between the plus and minus signs and the processes they represent.

Chapter 2: Internalizing Number Combinations to 10

Children work on developing facility with number combinations. The activities direct the children to explore, create, describe, and label number combinations as they occur in a variety of real-world situations.

Chapter 3: Developing Strategies for Adding and Subtracting

Children work with addition and subtraction problems in order to develop confidence, flexibility, and efficiency. The children practice applying various strategies as they develop ease and confidence in adding and subtracting.

Using the Book

Your use of this book will vary according to the needs of your children. The *Planning Guide* that accompanies this series offers specific information that can help you plan how to use this book's activities. The following are general suggestions for using the activities with different groups of children.

Kindergarten By the end of the kindergarten year, some children will be ready to begin acting out addition and subtraction story problems (Chapter 1) and to describe a number according to its parts (Chapter 2). For these children, de-emphasize the use of symbols and emphasize work with concrete objects.

First Grade Addition and subtraction are important mathematical topics for first grade and should be a central part of the math program for several months.

Second Grade Most second graders will have already worked with addition and subtraction. Some will have had hands-on experiences and others will have had lots of work with symbols. It will be important to ascertain the needs of your children in order to make decisions about which experiences to offer them. You can expect to find that more second graders will be ready to work with complex story problems than would first graders and that they will be ready to work with somewhat larger numbers and that they will not need to spend much time on learning to read and write equations. While second graders will be learning to add and subtract numbers to 100 (Book 3, Chapter 1) there should still be a major emphasis on internalizing number combinations to 10 (Book 2, Chapter 2) and developing strategies for working with numbers from 10 to 20 (Book 2, Chapter 3).

Third Grade You will probably find that the range of needs in your classroom is quite wide. Some third-grade children will still need to work with the activities in Chapters 2 and 3, focusing on numbers to 10. Others will need work interpreting complex problems and developing strategies for working with numbers to 20.

Children with Special Needs It is very important to give your children enough time to make sense of these beginning number relationships. Do not feel pushed to have them memorize relationships they don't really understand. A strong foundation will serve them in the long run. The charts "Meeting the Needs of Your Children" in the introduction to this book can help you choose appropriate activities.

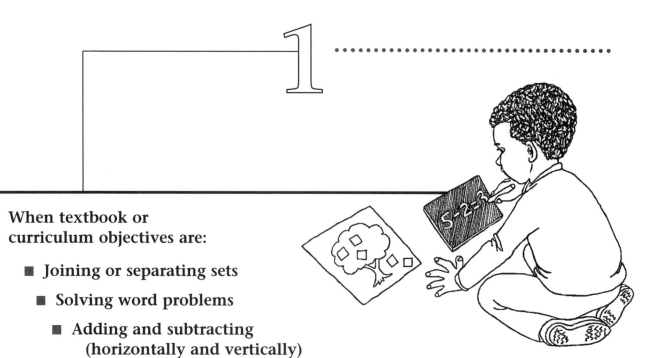

1

When textbook or
curriculum objectives are:

- ■ Joining or separating sets
- ■ Solving word problems
- ■ Adding and subtracting
  (horizontally and vertically)

Then you want to teach

Interpreting and Symbolizing Addition and Subtraction

Interpreting and Symbolizing Addition and Subtraction

The activities in this chapter introduce the processes of addition and subtraction through story problems that the children act out. Because the children need to learn to distinguish between the two processes, both addition and subtraction stories are included from the start in random order.

The first story situations you use should be simple, requiring either combining or separating groups of objects. Other more complex problems, such as those involving missing parts and comparative subtraction, are much more difficult for children to interpret and generally should not be used at an early stage. The following examples can help you determine which kind of problem is best for your children.

Here are three examples of simple story problems:

- *Addition with two addends* Four children were playing games in the park. Two more children joined them. How many children are playing games now?
- *Addition with more than two addends* Mykia went on a walk to look for pretty leaves. She picked up three red leaves, four gold leaves, and two brown leaves. How many leaves does she have?
- *Subtraction* The clown was holding seven balloons. He gave two of them away. How many does he have left?

Here are three examples of more complex story problems:

- *Equalizing* Abby has read six books so far this summer. Mollie has read four. In order to have read as many books as Abby, how many more does Mollie need to read?
- *Missing part* Up until this week's Little League game, Gene had made five runs this season. By the end of the game, he had a total of seven runs for the season. How many runs did he make during this week's game?
- *Comparative subtraction* Jessica found six rocks on the trail and Tia found seven. How many more rocks did Tia find than Jessica?

In large part, language and other developmental issues—rather than lack of instruction—determine which problems children will be able to interpret. Most young children are at a stage in their thinking at which simple addition and subtraction stories are most appropriate. It is important for children to think about and make sense of the problem situations in the stories you tell. If you give them situations they can make sense of, they will stay flexible in their thinking and will be willing to try to solve whatever problems they encounter. If you give them problems they don't understand and try to lead them through the problem situations, the children will stop trying to make sense for themselves and will, instead, begin to follow and imitate what you tell them to do.

There are ways to help prepare children for more complex story problems. For example, they can begin to work with the concept of how many more? (see Book One, Chapter Three, *The Concepts of More and Less*). They can practice taking numbers apart and figuring out the missing part, as they do in Chapter Two of this book. If you have children who are ready to work with more complex story problems or if you want more information about this level of work, refer to Working with Complex Addition and Subtraction Stories (activity 1–11).

Goals for Children's Learning*

Goals

Children will be able to make connections between the real world and the processes of addition and subtraction in a variety of situations by:

- Interpreting (acting out) addition and subtraction stories
- Reading and interpreting addition and subtraction cards and relating them to specific stories or actions
- Writing addition and subtraction equations to describe problems
- Writing story problems to go with equations

Analyzing and Assessing Children's Needs

Since we want children to understand addition and subtraction and use what they know to solve a variety of problems with confidence and efficiency, it is neither sufficient nor appropriate to determine their competence through exercises that merely require them to complete a page of problems. Instead, we can better find out what children understand about addition and subtraction through ongoing careful observations. When you introduce addition and subtraction to children and teach them to write equations, you will get valuable information about their learning if you pay close attention to the way they respond to tasks. The following questions will help you know what to look for as you watch children working on the activities in this chapter.

Questions to Guide Your Observations*

Questions

Interpreting Simple Story Problems

- Can the children interpret a simple addition and/or subtraction problem using physical models or drawings?
- Do they interpret the problem with ease or with difficulty? Do they need any prompts or hints?

* Adapted from *How Do We Know They're Learning? Assessing Math Concepts.*

- Do they need to listen to parts of the story and react to each part, or can they listen to the whole story and then act it out?
- Do they need to figure out the answer by counting, or do they anticipate the answer before acting it out?
- If they make a mistake, do they pay attention to their answer and self-correct if it doesn't make sense, or do they just report whatever they came up with?

Interpreting Equations

- Can the children interpret addition and/or subtraction equations using models?
- Can they read the equation?
- Do they confuse the plus and minus signs or forget to look at the signs?
- Can they make up a story to go with the equation?

Reading and Writing Equations

- Can the children write equations to describe story problems? Is this easy or challenging for them?
- Do the children need to write the numbers and symbols for each part of the story as they hear it, or can they write the entire equation after hearing the whole story?
- After writing an equation, can they read it back? Do they know how the numbers connect to the situation in the story?
- Do they use natural language (such as *and, is, take away*) or formal language (such as *plus, equals, subtract*)?
- If the children do not know how to use numbers and symbols to record in the conventional way, can they represent the story symbolically in some other way?

Size of Numbers

- Does the size of the numbers used in the stories seem to make any difference to the children's understanding or confidence?
- What size numbers is the child most comfortable using? 6 or less? 10 or less? up to 20?

Level of Complexity

- Can the children interpret simple addition and/or subtraction problems with ease?
- Can they act out complex problems that involve such concepts as missing parts or comparative subtraction?
- Which kinds of complex problems do they find easy? Which do they find challenging?

Meeting the Range of Needs

The activities in this chapter, designed as an introduction to addition and subtraction, provide the kind of practice most young children need. Even though most of your children may be working with the same tasks, they will not all be working at the same level at the same time.

The counting boards are a basic material that can be used, along with the addition and subtraction cards, at a variety of levels. The children will naturally move through several levels as they work with these materials, and you will have some children working at each of these levels at the same time.

For example, some children may be working with sums and differences for numbers to 6, while others will be ready to work with numbers to 10. (If you have duplicated the addition and subtraction cards to 6 and to 10 on paper of two different colors, it will be easy to direct individual children to take the materials of the colors appropriate for them.) At the same stations, some children will be reading and interpreting the addition and subtraction cards but doing no writing while others will be writing the equations as they figure out the sums and differences. Even the writing activities can be done at more than one level. At the basic level, children copy equations from the addition and subtraction cards. At a higher level, they write the equations without models.

If you have some children who are not ready to work with addition and subtraction equations, let them use the same materials as the rest of the class but adapt the way they use the materials. For example, some children could be merely counting out sets of cubes or Color Tiles onto the counting boards or matching groups and numerals while other children are using addition and subtraction cards with the boards.

If you have children who are ready for a greater challenge, you can ask them to make up their own equations using larger numbers or write stories to go with the equations.

Remember that having children use the same materials at a variety of levels helps build an acceptance of individual differences.

A Classroom Scene ....

Here we visit a classroom where the teacher, Mr. Bonilla, has introduced several independent activities that focus on beginning addition and subtraction. The children have had several days to work with them. The class knows the rules and procedures for independent work, and everyone is now familiar with today's activities. That gives the teacher a chance to meet with a small group of children while the others continue their independent work.

Independent and Small-Group Work:
Interpreting the Plus and Minus Signs

Mr. Bonilla has pulled aside a small group of children who need a bit more help before they can work with addition and subtraction cards on their own. He needs to make sure that the rest of the class is working productively before he begins the small-group lesson. So he asks the small group to practice writing numerals on individual chalkboards while they are waiting for their lesson to begin. Mr. Bonilla looks around to see if the other children have settled in and are getting to work.

Although it is early in the school year, the children have been carefully prepared for independent work, and they do well when the teacher is available to interact with them. At this time, Mr. Bonilla can focus more easily on a small group when he has a parent volunteer in the room to monitor the children as they work independently at stations. Later in the year, he will be able to pull out a small group even when he has no help. In the meantime, if he has no adult help when he needs to work with a small group, Mr. Bonilla sometimes limits the movement in the class by giving the other children particular tasks rather than setting up the stations and giving them choices.

Today, there is a parent volunteer, Patsy Chavez. She has observed the class a few times while the teacher was interacting with the children and she seems comfortable in that role. Mr. Bonilla encourages the parent volunteers to stand back and watch the children, intervening only when it seems necessary. He asks the parents to take notes on what they see, which helps them tune in to how the children get their own answers.

Mr. Bonilla takes a moment to watch as the children choose what they are going to work on. Most of the children are choosing to work with counting boards and addition and subtraction cards. These children are working at a variety of levels. Some are reading the cards and interpreting the problems with counters. A few are copying the problems and writing the answers.

Yesterday Mr. Bonilla spent the math period checking to see if the children were working at appropriate levels and making notes on his observations on a class recording sheet. He finds that most children choose the level for which they are ready, but occasionally he needs to redirect a child to a more appropriate task.

As he looks around, Mr. Bonilla sees several children playing games that give them practice distinguishing between the plus and minus signs (activities 1–13 through 1–15).

Four children are playing Race to Ten (activity 1–13). These children get excited and shout when they spin the spinner. Mr. Bonilla asks them to remember that he is working with a small group and needs them to work as quietly as they can. He has that station placed far away from where he is working with the small group because he knows the children always become a bit noisy when they play that game.

After a few moments, Mr. Bonilla turns his attention to the small group. "I see that it is getting easier for you to write numerals. Do you remember how hard it used to be when you were first learning? Erase your boards now; we won't be using them anymore today."

The teacher hands out 6" × 9" sheets of green construction paper, one to each child, to serve as counting boards. Then he places connecting cubes where everyone can reach them. When he asks for suggestions for what the green counting boards could stand for, the group decides it should be a nearby park.

Today Mr. Bonilla wants to find out if everyone in this group is able to act out addition and subtraction stories (activity 1–3). He begins, "Show me this story on your boards. Five children were playing at the park." He pauses for a minute so the children can get their counters. Then he goes on: "Two of them had to go home for lunch. How many children are still playing at the park?"

The teacher watches to see how the children approach the problem. Everyone except Jake counts out five counters and then removes two. Jake gets five and then two more. Natalie waits to see what the others are doing and then takes away two.

Mr. Bonilla quietly restates the problem for Jake. "Can you show me the five children?" Jake counts out five counters. "Now, have two of these children go home." Jake follows those directions successfully.

Mr. Bonilla now moves on to Modeling Addition and Subtraction Equations (activity 1–4). He tells the group, "Now I'm going to write the numbers that tell what happened in the park story. What do I need to write first?"

The children direct him to write "5."

"What do I need to write next?"

"Take away two," the children respond.

"And how many are left?"

"Three."

Mr. Bonilla continues to write equations as he tells a few more stories, some requiring addition and some requiring subtraction. Jake still hesitates before counting out his counters, but Natalie becomes more sure of herself and begins to act out the stories without first watching the other children.

Next, Mr. Bonilla holds up several addition and subtraction cards and has the children act them out (activity 1–5). Again he sees Jake having some problems and he notices Natalie watching the others to see what to do. Mr. Bonilla reviews the procedure for working independently with the counting boards (activity 1–12) and then asks the children to tell him what they will be doing. Taking turns, the children are able to explain the steps: choosing a set of counting boards and some counters, taking addition and subtraction cards from the bowl at the station, placing one card on each board, and using the counters to tell the story.

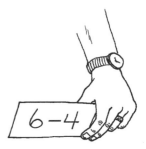

Mr. Bonilla has the children work for a while at the rug where they have been meeting. He offers Jake the option of working either with the addition and subtraction cards or with numeral cards for counting practice. Jake chooses the familiar numeral cards with some sense of relief. Mr. Bonilla waits for a minute to make sure everyone in the group has started to work. Then he walks around the classroom to see what is happening with the rest of the class, taking along his observation recording sheet so that he can make notes as needed.

Most of the children seem to be acting out the stories and interpreting the problems correctly. The teacher notices Scott (who is working with the subtraction card that shows $6 - 2$) starting to put more counters on his board and then remembering that he has to take some off instead. Then Mr. Bonilla hears Donna reminding Brittany, "No, no. That's a minus." He stops to watch Gina write an equation. She is writing slowly and deliberately with great concentration and gets it done correctly.

Luis is working with the counting boards that have a corral setting. Mr. Bonilla notices that Luis is adding all the time, even when he should be subtracting. Luis is new to the class and hasn't had as much experience working with mixed addition and subtraction. Mr. Bonilla didn't realize that Luis was still having trouble with this or he would have included him in the small-group work today. He stops to talk to Luis, but before he has a chance to say anything, Luis notices his own mistake and says, "Oh, no! I forgot all about doing take-aways. I was thinking too much about the animals I was putting in my corral. My dad is going to take me to see my grandpa this weekend. He lives on a farm. He has so many animals." Luis gets busy correcting his errors. Mr. Bonilla is reassured that this child just needed to be reminded to pay attention to the signs.

Walking back to check on the small group, the teacher is pleased with the children's work. He spots a few counting errors and reminds everyone to make sure they are counting correctly. They spontaneously look at their boards and begin checking.

Mr. Bonilla decides to let this group work along with the rest of the class at the independent stations tomorrow. He will keep his eye on Natalie and make sure she knows what to do. He will also spend a little time with Jake using the addition and subtraction cards, but will allow him to continue to use the numeral cards for independent practice.

About the Activities

Introducing the Processes of Addition and Subtraction

This chapter starts with teacher-directed activities for introducing addition and subtraction through story problems. Other teacher-directed activities help you model the writing of addition and subtraction equations to acquaint children with the conventional ways of recording these processes. The chapter includes many activities for independent practice with reading, interpreting, and writing addition and subtraction equations.

Distinguishing Between the Plus and Minus Signs

Because one of our goals is for children to be able to distinguish between the processes and the signs representing them, both addition and subtraction are presented together. When children are first learning to work with the plus (+) and minus (−) signs, they often confuse them. A number of teacher-directed activities and partner games are included to help children focus on the difference between the signs.

Don't worry if there is some confusion as the children work with addition and subtraction together; it is a natural part of learning. Children need a chance to sort things out, as long as there is help available if they need it. Even if you were to present only one process (traditionally addition) for a long period of time, you would still eventually have to introduce the other process and face the problem of some children confusing the two. The children are better served in the long run if they have the chance to sort out these processes early, before getting locked into one or the other.

Refer to the *Planning Guide for Developing Number Concepts* for further information on organizing the activities to meet the needs of your classroom.

Materials Preparation

The materials preparation has been kept as simple as possible. Generally, you will find the directions for making any needed materials described in the activities. However, there are certain basic materials that are used over and over again. One such material, used for many different activities, is the counting board.

Counting Boards [Blackline Masters #2–6]

Each set of counting boards consists of eight cards that represent a particular setting. The children put counters on these boards to represent various story situations. Make eight copies of each of the ten counting boards on tagboard. Color and laminate them if desired.

Listed below are ideas for things that counters can represent in each setting:

Counting Board	Ideas for Things To Be Represented
Tree	Apples, cherries, lemons, leaves
Ocean (pool, lake)	Boats, fish, shells, whales, children
Barn	Farm animals
Cave	Bears, monsters, bugs, bats
Corral (pasture)	Cows, horses, pigs, cowboys
Store	Various toys
Road	Cars, trucks, motorcycles, people, parade
House	People, things in the house
Garden	Vegetables, flowers
Grass (yard, field)	Bugs, children playing, flowers, butterflies

Additional settings can be created on various kinds of paper, as follows:

Sky (on blue paper)	Birds, airplanes, bugs
Night or outer space (on black paper)	Moon, pumpkins, stars, spaceships
Beach (on sandpaper)	Shells, children playing, rocks, crabs

When the counting boards are used in a teacher-directed activity, each child needs one board. If you have more than eight children in a group, make extra copies so that each child can have the same board. When children are working with the counting boards independently, each child needs a complete set of eight. The counting boards can be stored in clear bags or in pocket-type envelopes.

Number Cubes

The children can create a variety of addition and subtraction problems by rolling a variety of number cubes. The cubes can be made from plain wooden blocks by cutting pieces of foam or by covering commercially made cubes with blank stickers. Color-code the numerals so that you can distinguish between the cubes quickly and easily. You could, for example, mark the 0–4 cubes in green, the 4–9 cubes in red, the 0–5 cubes in blue, and the 1–6 cubes in black.

The activities in this chapter call for the following cubes:

0–4 (green) [Write "4" on two sides.]
4–9 (red)
0–5 (blue)
1–6 (black)

Number Lines [Blackline Masters #28–29]

Run off BLMs #28 and #29 on tagboard and cut apart. Make the number lines available to children whenever they need models for writing numerals.

The children use addition and subtraction cards for several different activities.

Addition Cards [Blackline Masters #64–68]

Sums to 6 (Horizontal Addition—#64, Vertical Addition—#65)

Sums of 7 to 9 (Horizontal Addition—#66, Vertical Addition—#67)

Sums of 10 (Horizontal and Vertical Addition—#68)

Make copies of the sums to 6 on paper of one color. Make copies of the sums of 7 to 9 and the sums of 10 on paper of a second color. Cut the cards apart.

Subtraction Cards [Blackline Masters #69–73]

Subtracting from 1 to 6 (Horizontal Subtraction—#69, Vertical Subtraction—#70)

Subtracting from 7 to 9 (Horizontal Subtraction—#71, Vertical Subtraction—#72)

Subtracting from 10 (Horizontal and Vertical Subtraction—#73)

Make copies of differences of up to 6 using the same color paper as you used for sums to 6, and make copies of the differences of from 7 to 9 and from 10 on the same color paper as you used for the corresponding sums.

Plus-or-Minus Spinner

To make the spinner, cut out a tagboard circle about six inches in diameter. The circle can be made by tracing around a large margarine tub lid. Cut out a tagboard square slightly larger than the circle. Poke holes through the center of the square and the center of the circle.

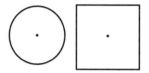

Draw a line from one corner of the square to the center. This line will serve as the pointer.

Draw a line through the center of the circle. Draw a plus sign on one side of the line and a minus sign on the other side.

Cut out three small squares (each measuring about $1\frac{1}{2}$ inches on a side) from the scraps of tagboard. Poke a hole through the center of each and crimp by pinching them. (The small squares will help create a space between the circle and the square base so that the spinner will spin easily.) Open a paper clip and push one end through the square, the three small squares, and the circle.

To keep the spinner from coming apart, and to keep children from sticking themselves, wrap a tiny piece of masking tape around the end of the paper clip. Make sure that the tape does not keep the spinner from spinning. Turn the spinner over and tape the base of the clip to the back of the square to secure the clip.

Teacher-Directed Activities

About Acting Out Addition and Subtraction Stories

In the following three activities, children act out the stories in a variety of ways. They sometimes actually perform the action described, such as stacking books or lining up. They might pretend to be the subjects of the story, such as frogs hopping or ladybugs crawling. They sometimes use counters, such as connecting cubes or Color Tiles, to represent the people, animals, or other objects in the story. Notice that by using counters, all the children can be actively engaged in interpreting the actions of the story.

Be sure to present the children with a mixture of addition and subtraction stories, sometimes using mathematical terms, sometimes not.

Whenever children are asked to act out a story in front of other children, always have the group direct them so that no individuals are "put on the spot."

TIP: *Using Both Mathematical and Natural Language in Story Problems*

One of your goals should be to acquaint your children with the language used in describing the actions of adding and subtracting: words like *altogether, total, in all, minus,* and *how many left.* However, it is very important that the children are always trying to make sense of the story and not just listening for "key" words. Therefore, you will sometimes want to use mathematical terms and other times non-mathematical terms. The following is a story told both ways.

- **Using mathematical terms:** Linda stacked three books on the table. She *added* one more book to the stack. How many books are in the stack *altogether*?
- **Using natural language:** Linda stacked three books on the table. She piled one more book on the stack of books. How many books are in the stack now?

The use of natural language, along with actual objects, reinforces the connection between the real world and the mathematics the children are learning. When children are introduced to the processes in this way, they will see them as everyday events and not just as tasks to be done in school.

Your children should be able to interpret both kinds of language with ease before you introduce them to any of the math symbols.

Materials: Objects readily available in the room.

Present addition and subtraction stories based on classroom materials such as books, chairs, and pencils. Call on children to act out each story. Substitute your children's names for the names in the following example:

Alice put four rulers on the table. Jim put two more rulers on the table. How many rulers are on the table? (addition)

* Based on *Mathematics Their Way*, "Word Problems Using Children and Props," p. 204.

Additional examples:

Nan, Jack, Brad, and Lea are working at the table. Jack and Lea are excused to go outside. How many children are still working? (subtraction)

Susanne, Laurie, and Todd are standing by the window. Tom and Kathy walk over to join them. How many children are standing by the window? (addition)

Dylan, Irene, Jenny, Nadia, and Roberto were sitting in a circle on the rug. Jenny and Roberto left the circle. How many children stayed on the rug? (subtraction)

Pooja had eight crayons in her box. She took out the red one and the yellow one. How many crayons are left in the box? (subtraction)

Six children are standing in line by the door. Four children are standing in line by the water fountain. How many children are there in both lines? (addition)

There were eight pencils in the pencil can. Emilio took out two of them. How many pencils are in the can now? (subtraction)

Alex lined up six word cards on the chalk tray. Tillie took away four of them. How many cards were left? (subtraction)

Lu Anne poured three cups of water into the tub. Yoshi added three more cupfuls. Charlene added two more cupfuls. How many cups were in the tub in all? (addition)

Adonia stacked up three books on the desk. Paulo stacked up four books. How many books were there altogether? (addition)

Materials: None required.

Tell addition and subtraction stories in which the children can pretend to be a variety of people, animals, or objects. Remember to include mathematical terms in some of the stories. Because your goal is to relate the processes of addition and subtraction to the real world, you may think that having children pretend is inappropriate. Be assured, however, that the use of fantasy can provide children with more opportunities to experience addition and subtraction than the other, more usual, classroom activities. Present the following example:

Adam, Timmy, Garland, and Freda are candles on a birthday cake. Mina blows three of the candles out. How many are still burning? (subtraction)

Additional examples:

Cindy, Bill, Andy, and Casey are clowns at a circus. Judy, Steven, and Jeff are more clowns who come to join the circus. How many clowns in all are in the circus? (addition)

There are nine bees buzzing around the flowers—Shawna, Cara, Lindsay, Eleanor, Eduardo, Galen, Danielle, Becky, and Mike. Three of the bees—Danielle, Becky, and Mike—fly back to the beehive. How many bees are still buzzing around the flowers? (subtraction)

James, Michelle, David, and Tereza are sailboats on the lake. Joel and Ash are rowboats on the lake. How many boats are on the lake? (addition)

Sissy, Mark, and Nicky are birds sitting in a tree. Mark and Sissy fly away. How many birds are left in the tree? (subtraction)

Materials: Counters, sorted by color · Counting boards (8 of the same board for each child) [BLMs #2–6] or Blank paper

Tell stories that children can model using counters to represent people, animals, or objects. Use a set of counting boards to represent a specific setting or use blank paper to represent any other setting. Make up a story to match each setting. Say, for example:

Today we are going to make up stories using corrals. What animals could be in our corrals?

> Horses.
>
> Cows.
>
> Pigs.
>
> There could be cowboys in there, too.

There are five horses in the corral. Three of them are taken out to the pasture. How many horses are left in the corral? (subtraction)

Clear your boards so we can tell a different story.

There were three pigs in the corral. The farmer went to the market and bought three more. How many pigs did he have altogether? (addition)

* Based on *Mathematics Their Way,* "Word Problems Using Blocks and Paper," p. 206.

Additional examples:

There were seven apples on the tree. A farmer came along and picked five of the apples. How many apples are still on the tree? (subtraction)

Counting board

Four ladybugs were crawling in the grass. Three more came to join them. How many ladybugs were there then? (addition)

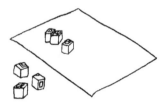

Counting board

There were six cars in the parking lot at Palace Market. Three of them were driven away. How many cars are left? (subtraction)

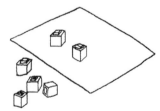

Blank paper

We gave our hamster, Tippy, six sunflower seeds. She ate four of them. How many seeds are left? (subtraction)

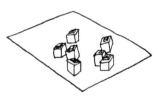

Blank paper

Four children were playing in the sandbox. Three more children came to play with them. How many children are in the sandbox? (addition)

Blank paper

Materials: None required.

Once the children are able to act out the stories you tell, begin modeling how to write equations to describe the stories. The children do not need to have had any previous experience reading and writing the plus, minus, and equals signs. The symbols will come to have meaning for the children when they watch you write the equations as they act out your stories.

Write some equations horizontally, others vertically, so that children become familiar with both.

Make sure you help the children connect the symbols with the story by having them tell how the numbers remind them of the story.

Addition Example:

Mercedes, Elias, Lupe, and Maria are in line to jump rope.
How many children are in line?... Yes, four.

Write "4" on the chalkboard.

Derek and Kevin got in line to jump rope, too. How many got in line?... Yes, two.

Write "+ 2."

How many children are in line?... Yes, six.

Write "= 6."

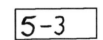

This is one way to write about the story we just acted out. It says, "Four and two is six." Four children and two children are six children altogether.

Subtraction Example:

There were five muffins on the plate. How many muffins is that?... Yes, five.

Write "5."

Tony took three of the muffins. How many did Tony take?... Yes, three.

Write "− 3."

How many muffins are left?... Yes, two muffins are left.

Write "= 2."

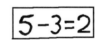

This is one way to write about the story we just acted out. It says, "Five take away three is two. Five muffins take away three muffins leaves two muffins."

TIP: *Relating Equations to the Actions in Story Problems*

As you present story problems, children should be given opportunities to record the actions in the stories through pictures and other informal representations as well as to learn to represent these stories with conventional symbols. The symbols should be introduced as a way of keeping track of the numbers and actions of the stories.

There is a natural tendency for young children to separate symbols from the experiences they represent. It is essential that your students come to see these symbols as ways of writing down their experiences. Therefore, after the equations have been written, read them back to the children using their natural language to encourage the connection of the symbols to the story being acted out. For example, suppose your students have acted out a story using cubes to represent children. After you have written the equation $4 + 2 = 6$, for example, read it back as "Four children and two children is six children" and say that the symbols help us remember the important numbers in the story.

After they have had many experiences, and when the children are confident about interpreting an equation as it relates to the situation in a story, introduce them to the more formal way of reading the equation; for example, "Four plus two equals six." From then on, use both natural language and the formal mathematical way of reading equations.

Whenever you present a story problem and write an equation for it, continue to ask the children how the equation relates to the story. For example, suppose the children act out this story with counters:

Six children were playing on the swings. Two went home for lunch. How many children are still playing?

Even when the children can correctly read the equation you write for this story, $6 - 2 = 4$, as "six minus two equals four," they should also be able to tell you what the numbers remind them of. A child may say, for example, "That tells that six kids were on the swings and then two had to go, and now there are four left."

Materials: Counters, sorted by color · Blank paper or Counting boards (1 per child) [BLMs #2–6]

After the children have had several experiences seeing you write equations to describe stories, encourage them to tell stories to describe equations. Start by writing an equation on the board. Have them act out their stories using manipulatives. For example:

Write "3 + 2 = 5."

To describe 3 + 2 = 5, children may say:

> **I have three white kittens and two black kittens. That means I have five kittens.**

> **There were three bears in the woods and two more came. Now there are five bears in the woods.**

Be sure to offer both addition and subtraction equations so that the children have frequent opportunities to distinguish between the two. For example:

Write "6 − 2 = 4."

To describe 6 − 2 = 4, children may say:

> **I saw six birds in the tree. Two birds flew away and then there were four left.**

> **There were six firefighters on the fire truck. Two firefighters went home. Four were still there.**

For a related independent activity, see Counting Boards: Reading Equations (activity 1–12).

* Based on *Mathematics Their Way,* "Interpreting Symbols," p. 217.

About the Plus and Minus Signs

In the following three small-group activities, children practice distinguishing between the plus and minus signs and performing the actions that the signs represent. Notice that the emphasis is entirely on the symbols and their corresponding actions. (No sums or differences are being determined.)

Teach the games, first using the terms *get more* and *take away*; then introduce the words *plus* and *minus* as other ways of saying the same things.

For related independent activities, see Race to Ten (activity 1–13), Plus-and-Minus Train (activity 1–14), and Clear the Deck (activity 1–15).

1–6 Roll and Count .... Small-Group Activity

Materials: Counters • Plus-or-Minus Spinner (See Materials Preparation, p. 15.) • 1–6 Number cubes (See Materials Preparation, p. 14.) • Working-space papers (1 or 2 per child) [BLM #1]

The children take turns spinning the spinner and rolling the number cube. Each child adds counters to or subtracts them from his or her working-space paper according to what they spin and roll. For example:

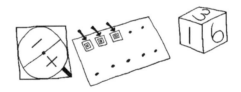

That's a plus, and I rolled a three—plus three.

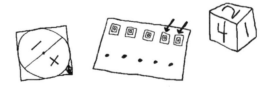

Another plus. I need two more—plus two.

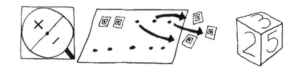

I got a minus. I rolled a three. That's minus three.

If the spinner and number cube indicate that children are to take away more counters than they have on their papers, then children should say "not enough" and spin again. If the spinner and number cube indicate that children are to add more counters than they have room for, the children should each take an additional working-space paper.

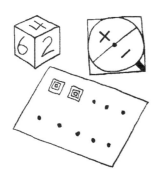

Minus four—not enough!

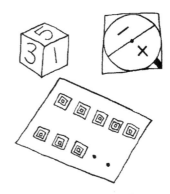

Plus five. I need another paper.

1–7 Listen and Count* .... Small-Group Activity

Materials: Counters • Working-space papers (1 or 2 per child) [BLM #1] • Plus-or-Minus Spinner (See Materials Preparation, p. 15) • Bell (or xylophone)

The children take turns spinning the spinner to determine the operation to be performed. Ring the bell several times to indicate the number of counters that children should add to, or take away from, their working-space papers. If the number to be taken away is larger than the number of counters on their papers, the children say, "Not enough!" If the number to be added is greater than the number of spaces left on their working-space papers, each child should take another paper.

Ding. Ding.

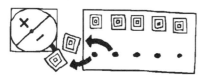

Minus two.

Ding. Ding. Ding.

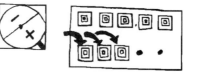

Plus three.

* Based on *Mathematics Their Way,* "Listen and Count," p. 190.

Materials: Counters · Working-space papers (1 or 2 per child) [BLM #1] · 1–6 Number cube (See Materials Preparation, p. 14.)

The children take turns rolling the number cube to determine the number of counters to show on their working-space papers. Each time they roll, they verbalize what they have to do to change their previous number of counters to show the new number. Write the appropriate symbols for each roll as children describe what they need to do. For example:

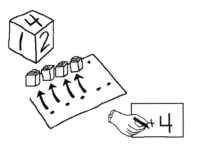

We rolled a four. We need to get four. Plus four.

Write "+ 4."

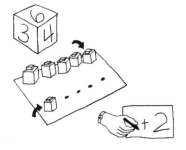

We rolled a six. We need two more to make six—that's plus two.

Write "+ 2."

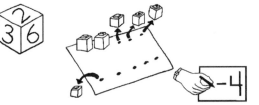

We rolled a two. We need to take four counters off. That's minus four.

Write "– 4."

NOTE: In this activity, as opposed to Roll and Count (activity 1–6), the number rolled indicates not how many to add or subtract, but rather how many to show on the working-space paper. Some children will have difficulty switching between the two activities. However, it is essential that children become flexible in their thinking and learn to deal with number in a variety of ways. It is important for them to play both these games. But be sensitive to their potential confusion and help the children by reminding them as often as necessary how each game is played.

Materials: Counters, sorted by color • Counting boards [BLMs #2–6] • Small chalkboard, chalk, and eraser for each child

Level 1: **Copying Equations**

When the children are ready to begin writing equations, continue having them act out addition and subtraction stories using counters and counting boards. As they work, write the equation that describes the action in the story on the board. The children can copy this equation on their individual chalkboards.

Level 2: **Writing and Checking**

As the children act out addition or subtraction stories, have them write the equation that describes the story without the help of a model. Then, write the equation on the board so that they can check their work. For example:

There are five apples on a tree.
Jamie picks two.
How many are left?

For a related independent activity, see *Writing Equations with Counting Boards (activity 1–16).*

Materials: Counters, sorted by color · Blank paper or Counting boards [BLMs #2–6]
(1 per child) · Writing paper and pencil for each child
For the variation: Duplicate the Counting boards [BLMs #2–6] for use as worksheets.

Write an equation on the board. Ask the children to make up a story to match it
and then to act out their story with counters and counting boards. After the children have had turns telling their stories, model how to write their words on the
board as a story problem. For example, for "5 + 1 = 6," a child may tell this story:

My mother gave me five chicken nuggets
last night, and then I asked for one more.

Additional examples for 5 + 1 = 6:

I brought the teacher five daisies, and
Marcus brought her one rose.

We had five puppets in the classroom,
and I brought in one more.

Variation: The children could make a drawing to illustrate the equation story they
write. Discuss with them various ways they could show subtraction in a drawing.

NOTE: Many children will find it difficult to ask the question that turns their story
into a problem. They may need a prompt, such as "How many are there?" or "How
many are left?"

Ther are six giraffes. Two got taken
to the Zoo. How meny are left?

You may choose to distribute "worksheet" copies of the counting boards so that the
children can illustrate and write their stories directly on the worksheets.

For a related independent activity, see Writing Stories To Match Equations (activity 1–17).

Materials: Counters or real objects.

Tell stories describing various addition and subtraction situations and have the children act them out.

Unlike the stories presented in previous activities, which included the simple combining and separating of sets, these stories ask children to work with more complex situations that may involve the use of missing addends and comparative subtraction. It is important for children to think about and make sense of the problem situations in the stories you tell. Resist leading the children through the problem situations, as this may cause children to stop trying to make their own sense of them. Watch carefully to see how the children use the manipulatives to work out the following types of problems, as this will be a clue to their level of thinking. If they are unable to make sense of these situations after seeing you and other children act them out, continue to provide opportunities for them to see others act them out, but do not expect them to do the work on their own as yet.

Equalizing

Mark made six clay bowls in his art class. Carrie made four bowls. How many more will Carrie have to make to have the same number of bowls as Mark?

Missing Part (Missing Addend)

Rosalie is supposed to make sure that there are six chairs at the round table. There are already three chairs at the table. How many more chairs does Rosalie need to get?

Deane checked out six books from the library. Four of the books were about dogs and the rest were about horses. How many books were about horses?

There were seven pieces of fruit in the bowl this morning. Now only four are left. How many were taken?

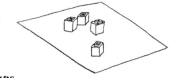

Vicki has seven dogs at her house. Two of the dogs are grown-ups. How many dogs are puppies?

Jenna has a doll collection. She got two dolls for her birthday and now she has eight dolls. How many dolls did she have just before her birthday?

I saw six children waiting at the bus stop. When I came back later, only three of them were still waiting. How many children left the bus stop?

Comparative Subtraction

Lian picked out eight books from the classroom library. Trish picked out five. How many more did Lian pick out than Trish?

Lian's books

Trish's books

There are five horses and three cows in the field. How many more horses are there than cows?

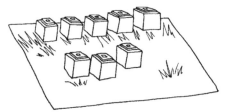

A seven-car freight train was carrying freight to the city. A five-car passenger train was going to the city, too. How much longer was the freight train than the passenger train?

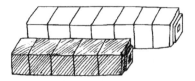

Independent Activities

Materials: Counters, sorted by color • Counting boards (8 of the same board for each child) [BLMs #2–6] • Addition and Subtraction cards [BLMs #64–73]

Each child takes a set of counting boards, a container of counters, and a set of addition and subtraction cards. Then the child spreads out the eight boards and puts an addition or subtraction card with each board. The child decides what the counters will represent and then places them on the boards in groups to represent the problems shown on the cards.

When working with subtraction, children place the counters they "take away" below the corresponding numeral on the subtraction card.

Materials: Counters • Plus-or-Minus Spinner (See Materials Preparation, p. 15.) • 1–6 Number cubes (1 per pair) (See Materials Preparation, p. 14.) • Working-space papers (1 or 2 per child) [BLM #1]

This is a game that helps children practice distinguishing between the plus and minus signs and performing the corresponding operation. Each player starts with an empty working-space paper. Players use counters to cover the dots on their papers. Their goal is be the first to cover all ten dots.

The players spin the spinner to determine whether to add (put counters onto their papers) or to subtract (take counters off). They roll the number cube to see how many counters to add or subtract. The players take turns, each moving counters only in response to his or her *own* spin and roll.

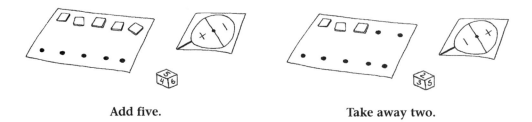

Add five.   Take away two.

If the spinner and the number cube indicate that a player is to take away more counters than are on the working-space paper, then the player misses a turn.

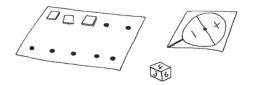

I can't take off four. I don't have enough. I lose my turn.

If a spin and roll indicate that a player is to add more counters than there is room for on the paper, the player may take another working-space paper.

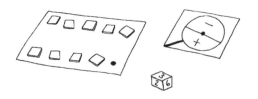

I need to add three. I have to get another working-space paper.

The children continue to taking turns until one player's turn ends with exactly ten counters on his or her first paper. The player who gets ten first wins the game.

.... **Independent Activity for Partners**

Materials: Connecting cubes (one color) · Plus-and-Minus Train game board (1 per child) made from Number-Train Outlines (10) [BLM #98] · 1–6 Number cube (1 per pair) · Plus-or-Minus Spinner (1 per pair)

Preparation: To make Plus-and-Minus Train game boards, duplicate BLM #98 and cut apart the number trains. For each game board, mount two number-train outlines, end to end, on a tagboard strip about 2" × 16" long.

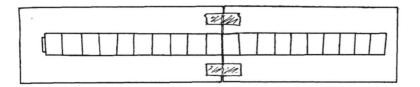

This is a game that helps children practice distinguishing between the plus and minus signs and helps them to perform the corresponding operations.

The players begin by each putting 20 cubes on a game board. Each one's goal is to be the first to completely clear his or her board.

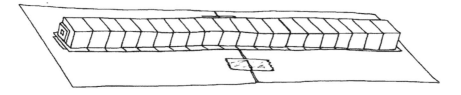

Each player, in turn, rolls the number cube and spins the spinner to see whether to add cubes or to take them off his or her own game board.

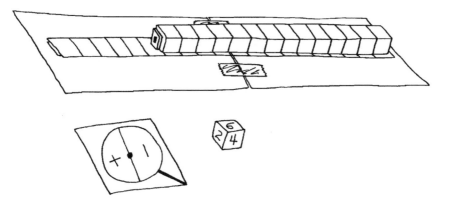

I rolled a minus six. I took six off.

If a player's roll and spin calls for adding more cubes than there are spaces available on the game board, then that player loses a turn.

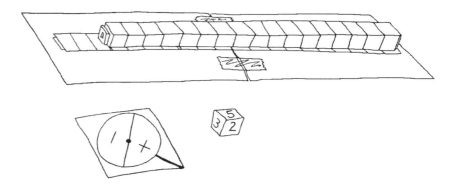

Oh no, I rolled a plus five! I can't fit five more on. I lose my turn.

The first player to clear a game board completely is the winner.

1–15 Clear the Deck

.... **Independent Activity for Partners**

Materials: Counters · Clear-the-Deck Game Board (1 per child) [BLM #74] · Number cubes 1–6 or 4–9 (1 per pair) · Plus-or-Minus Spinner (1 per pair)
Preparation: Cut each copy of BLM #74 along the dotted line to make two game boards, each with two ten-shapes.

This is a game that is intended to provide children with opportunities to distinguish between the plus and minus signs and to perform the corresponding operation.

The children begin by filling each game board with 20 counters. Their goal is to be the first to completely "Clear the Deck," or clear off the board.

Notice that for each turn some children will be paying attention to the numbers that result and others will be focused only on what to add or take away.

Players take turns spinning the spinner and rolling the number cube to see whether to add counters or to take them off their game board. For example:

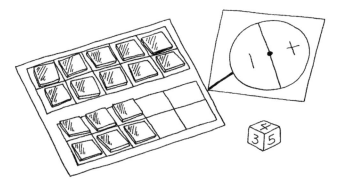

The spinner says minus. I rolled a four. I take four off.

If the number of counters a player spins and rolls won't fit on the game board, that player loses a turn.

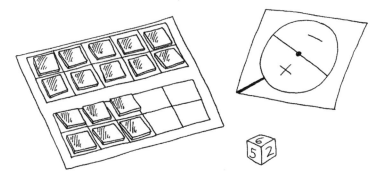

I rolled plus six. I don't have spaces for six. I lose my turn.

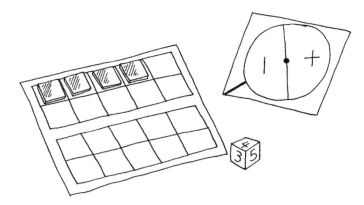

I got a minus and I rolled four. I can "clear the deck." I win!

Materials: *Level 1:* Counters, sorted by color · Addition and Subtraction cards [BLMs #64–73] · Counting boards (8 of the same board per child) [BLMs #2–6] · 2" × 6" strips of paper (8 per child)
Level 2: Same as for Level 1, but without Addition and Subtraction cards.

After the children have had practice writing equations for teacher-directed stories (see Writing Equations To Label Addition and Subtraction Stories, activity 1–9), they can begin writing equations for their own stories with the help of addition and subtraction cards and counting boards. This activity can be done over and over again. The children will remain interested because each time they work with the boards they can choose different settings and pretend that the counters are people, objects, or animals.

Level 1: Copying Equations

Each child chooses a set of counting boards and gets a container of counters, eight addition and subtraction cards, and eight 2" × 6" strips of paper. The child spreads out the counting boards, places one addition or subtraction card with each board, and puts counters on each board according to what appears on the card. Then, on strips of paper, the child writes completed problems to record the work on the boards. When this has been done for all eight boards, the child staples the strips of papers together to form a small book.

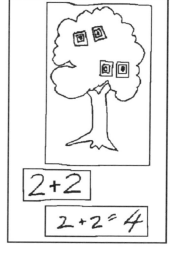

I have two apples on the top of my tree and four more under them.

Six squirrels were in a tree. Then three ran down to the ground.

There were two birds who landed in the tree. Then two more birds landed next to them.

Level 2: **Writing Equations**

The child no longer uses the addition and subtraction cards but makes up his or her own story problem for each counting board. The child writes a completed equation on a 2" × 6" strip of paper. You can limit the numbers used by telling the children to use no more than ten counters for each story.

Six children were playing in the grass. Two went home. Four are left.

Materials: Counters, sorted by color · Blank paper or Counting boards [BLMs #2–6] · Addition and Subtraction cards [BLMs #64–73] · Writing paper and pencil for each child

Children choose addition and subtraction cards and make up matching number stories working with the counters and the counting boards. The children then write their story.

Variation: One child reads aloud a story that has been written by another child, uses counters to act out the story, and then writes the equation that represents it.

3+3=6

There were three eagles.
Three more landed on a branch,
then there were six.

For a related teacher-directed activity, see Writing Stories To Go with Equations (activity 1–10).

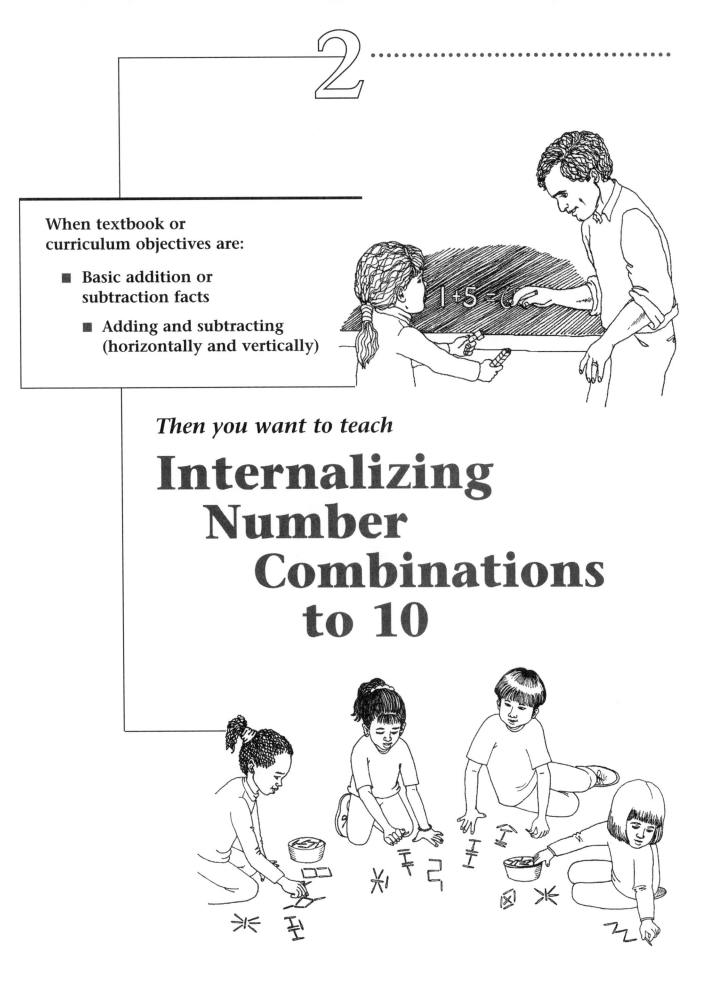

2

When textbook or curriculum objectives are:

- Basic addition or subtraction facts

- Adding and subtracting (horizontally and vertically)

Then you want to teach

Internalizing Number Combinations to 10

Internalizing Number Combinations to 10

It may seem that the work children do with number combinations to ten is not as important or challenging as the work they do with larger numbers. However, this work is critical to building a strong math foundation that will serve children in the future. If children can break up any number (to ten) and put the parts together again with ease, they will be able to work with larger numbers in flexible and powerful ways.

Consider the following example, which shows how children might use their knowledge of basic relationships to figure out a problem such as 74 − 36.

70 take away 30 is 40.

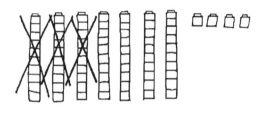

I can take 6 ones away from one of the tens. That leaves 4 ones.

The 3 tens and 4 ones make 34.

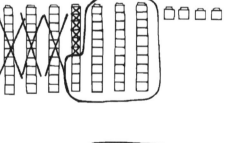

I still have the 4 ones I started with. I need to put those 4 back with the 34 to make 38.

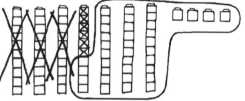

The basic relationships that the child has to know to do this problem with ease are 7 − 3 = 4 (for 7 tens minus 3 tens is 4 tens), 10 − 6 = 4, and 4 + 4 = 8.

Another way a child might figure out the difference between the two numbers is by "adding up." The child might say, "If I add 40 to 36, that would be 76. But I only need to get to 74, so I'll take the extra 2 off the 40 and that makes 38." The basic relationships that this child used were 3 + 4 = 7 (for 3 tens and 4 tens make 7 tens), 6 − 4 = 2, and 10 − 2 = 8.

Those of us who memorized basic facts without knowing to look for number relationships may have difficulty following the thinking of those who use these relationships to solve problems. However, second- and third-grade children who are given opportunities to look for relationships are able to so with ease and confidence. If children are going to be able to use number combinations with understanding, they need experiences that will help them discover and internalize these basic relationships.

Memorizing basic facts, perhaps with the use of flash cards, is very different from internalizing number combinations. *Memorized* knowledge is knowledge that can be forgotten. *Internalized* knowledge can't be forgotten because it is a part of the way we see the world. Children who memorize addition and subtraction facts often forget what they have learned. On the other hand, children who have internalized a concept or relationship can't forget it; they know it *has* to be that way because of a whole network of relationships and interrelationships that they have discovered and constructed in their minds.

For example, children know that 6 and 7 is 13 because it *has to be*. It has to be because it represents relationships that make sense. It has to be 13 because 6 and 6 is 12 and 7 is 1 more than 6, so 6 + 7 must be 1 more than 12.

They know that 6 + 7 *has to be* 13 because you can make a 10 if you take 4 off the 7 and put the 4 with the 6. You then have 3 left to combine with the 10 to make 13.

They know that 6 + 7 *has to be* 13 because 7 and 7 is 14. Six is 1 less than 7, so 6 + 7 has to be 1 less than 14.

Learning these basic relationships is a long and complex process, and we are often unaware of all that young children are figuring out as they work to learn these basic combinations. The first step for the young child is recognizing that numbers are composed of smaller numbers. This is not obvious to them. If you ask kindergarten children or even beginning first graders to identify the number of toothpicks in the parts of a toothpick design, you will find many who will be puzzled.

If you tell a child at that stage of thinking, "Oh, I see three and two in your design," the child might say, "That's not three and two. That's five. See—one, two, three, four, five." To this child, five is five, and that's that!

Later, children will begin to see the smaller parts that make up a number and will be able to describe them, although they will not necessarily remember which parts make up a particular number. At this stage, they won't even notice inconsistencies; they will just assume that they have found a different way. For example, the child who made the following designs believes he has found many different ways to arrange six toothpicks and does not realize that he has made an error.

I can make lots of designs of six.
See, there's three and three . . . two and two and two . . . and three and four.

Over time, given enough experiences with combinations of six, the children will begin to recognize that particular combinations come up again and again. They will see for themselves, for example, that three plus three and three plus four cannot both describe six.

We must not rush our children through these important experiences; rather, we must give them the time they need to build this foundation.

Goals for Children's Learning*

| Goals |

Children will take numbers apart and put them back together in a variety of ways and will be able to:

- Describe the parts of many different number arrangements
- Describe the parts of numbers to 10 using symbols
- Determine the whole when the parts of a number are known
- Determine a missing part of a number when the other part is known
- Find all the ways a number can be broken up into two or more parts

* Adapted from *How Do We Know They're Learning? Assessing Math Concepts.*

Analyzing and Assessing Children's Needs ....

The goals we have for children's learning go beyond simply having children memorize basic facts. When we want to determine what children really understand about number combinations, it is not enough to know if they can fill in answers on worksheets or timed tests. Instead, we need to know if they can take numbers apart and put them together in many different ways.

The Hiding Assessment is particularly helpful in establishing what children know about number combinations. It will provide you with the information you need to determine the appropriate number or range of numbers for children who are working with number combinations. This individual assessment can be done quickly and will give you extremely valuable information that is hard to get any other way.

In this assessment, the child is asked to determine the missing part of a number (to 10) when shown one part of that number. Being asked to visualize a missing part of a number is much more difficult than many of us realize. Presenting children with this challenge gives us valuable insights into their knowledge of number combinations.

The Hiding Assessment

Begin by asking the child to hand you a number of counters. It generally works to start with five. Hide some of the counters in one hand and display those that remain in your other hand.

Ask, "How many are hiding?"

Keeping the total of five counters, hide a different number in one hand, displaying the remainder in the other hand.

Again ask, "How many are hiding?"

Repeat the activity with several different combinations of five.

After the child responds by telling how many he or she thinks are hiding, be sure not to show the child the hidden counters, as this would provide information that would allow the child to temporarily do better, thus clouding your assessment.

If the child is successful in naming combinations of five, check his or her ability to work with larger numbers in the same way. If the child is unsuccessful with five, check his or her ability to work with smaller numbers.

Some children will have little or no success with five, yet they will know how to find combinations of four quickly and easily. (Even one more or less makes a big difference in this assessment.)

When you work with numbers larger than six, children will need time to count to see how many you are showing them. Then you want to see if they are able to tell the missing number quickly and confidently, or if they need time to figure it out.

The Hiding Assessment Recording Sheet that follows is available as blackline master #75, which can be found on page 205.

The Hiding Assessment

The child determines the missing parts of numbers (up to 10) when shown one part.

Child's Name _____

Assessment Procedures	Observations		
	Date_____	Date_____	Date_____
Ask the child to hand you a particular number of counters. When assessing a child for the first time, ask the child to hand you five counters. Hide some of the counters in one hand and show the child the remaining counters in your other hand. Ask, "How many are hiding?" Change the number of counters that you are "hiding" and ask, "Now, how many are hiding?" Repeat for several combinations for that number.	Number _____ ____ Makes no response or says, "I don't know." ____ Says an unreasonable number. ____ Tells a number that is close but inaccurate. ____ Figures out how many are hiding. ____ Knows quickly and confidently.	Number _____ ____ Makes no response or says, "I don't know." ____ Says an unreasonable number. ____ Tells a number that is close but inaccurate. ____ Figures out how many are hiding. ____ Knows quickly and confidently.	Number _____ ____ Makes no response or says, "I don't know." ____ Says an unreasonable number. ____ Tells a number that is close but inaccurate. ____ Figures out how many are hiding. ____ Knows quickly and confidently.
If the child is successful with the number you are assessing, check larger numbers in the same way. If the child is unsuccessful with that number, check smaller numbers.	Number _____ ____ Makes no response or says, "I don't know." ____ Says an unreasonable number. ____ Tells a number that is close but inaccurate. ____ Figures out how many are hiding. ____ Knows quickly and confidently.	Number _____ ____ Makes no response or says, "I don't know." ____ Says an unreasonable number. ____ Tells a number that is close but inaccurate. ____ Figures out how many are hiding. ____ Knows quickly and confidently.	Number _____ ____ Makes no response or says, "I don't know." ____ Says an unreasonable number. ____ Tells a number that is close but inaccurate. ____ Figures out how many are hiding. ____ Knows quickly and confidently.

Guide to Children's Responses*

- **Makes no response**

  This indicates that the number is too big to think about or that the child cannot visualize the hidden parts.

- **Makes inappropriate response**

  At a certain stage, children will just say a number that may be even bigger than the number worked with.

- **Response is close to the correct answer, but inaccurate**

  Even though the child may be wrong, saying a number that is a possible answer shows some developing number sense.

- **Figures it out**

  Being able to figure out a number is a sign of growth, but it is not an indication that the child knows the combinations.

- **Knows quickly and confidently**

  When the child gives an automatic response, he or she has internalized the combinations.

You can also learn much about what children understand about number combinations by observing them while they work. The following questions will guide your observations as you watch the children at work on the activities in this chapter.

* Adapted from *A Look at Children's Thinking.* (Video II) *Assessment Techniques: Number Combinations and Place Value.*

Questions to Guide Your Observations*

Describing the Parts of a Number

- Can the children name the parts of a number if the numbers are modeled with manipulatives? Can they describe the parts if they are distinguished by color? by position?
- Can they describe a number in more than one way?
- Can they label the parts of the numbers with symbols?

Finding All the Possible Combinations

- Can the children find different possible combinations for a number when using manipulatives?
- Do they make sure all the ways they find are different from the others, or do they repeat some of the same ways?
- Do they organize their work in any way? Can they tell if they have found all the possible ways?
- Can they think of all the combinations when no physical models are present?

Telling the Missing Part of a Number

- Can the children name the missing part of a number when shown one part?
- Which numbers to ten can they work with successfully?
- If they do not know how to name a missing part, do they guess or do they realize that they don't know?
- Do they need time to figure out an answer, or do they know it quickly?

Meeting the Range of Needs

The activities designed to help children learn number combinations can be made easier or harder simply by a change in the size of the number being worked with. Because children can do the same task with different numbers, children working at various levels can work side by side.

The way children approach the tasks will vary. For example, when children have been asked to find all the number combinations they can for a given number, some will systematically search for ways to make other combinations, others will not. Some will find many combinations, others will not. Some will be able to keep organized records of what they find, others will not. Some children will be ready to work with symbols before others. You can meet the range of needs simply by providing children with many opportunities to work with the manipulatives.

* Adapted from *How Do We Know They're Learning? Assessing Math Concepts.*

A Classroom Scene ....

Ms. Lee's first-grade class is learning and describing the parts of numbers through number arrangement activities (2–14 through 2–17). The children are working with a variety of manipulatives, including connecting cubes, toothpicks, Color Tiles, wooden cubes, and collections of buttons and bread tags. This set of tasks is open-ended. The children are to create as many different arrangements as they can. They have been working on this set of activities for several days. It always takes three or four days for the children to become really comfortable with how to do the tasks and with what is expected of them. Most children now know what to do, so they are ready to focus on learning from the tasks.

Independent Stations: *Creating Number Arrangements*

As Ms. Lee looks around the classroom, the children are working hard, engaged in the tasks. With everyone busy, she will be able to support those few children who need help in accomplishing their work. The teacher takes a clipboard to make notes about what she learns as she watches individuals at work.

Some children have already made several arrangements. Others are having a difficult time getting started. The teacher walks over to Matthew who, along with several other children, is working with connecting cubes.

Matthew has made three trains of five and is now staring at them. When Ms. Lee comes over he says, "I can't think of any more."

Ms. Lee wants to help Matthew realize that there are lots of ways to make cube trains of five. She asks him to look at one of his trains and to think about how he might change it to make a different one: "I see one of your trains has all the blue cubes touching. Do you think you can make trains in which the blue cubes aren't touching?" To let Matthew know that she expects him to get more work done, she says, "I'll be back in a few minutes to see how many you have made."

Ms. Lee then walks over to check on Rusty, who is working with the wooden cubes. He has made an arrangement using six cubes.

Ms. Lee points out the number combination that Rusty has made. "There is three and three," she says.

"No, that's six," the boy tells her. "See? One, two, three, four, five, six."

Rusty's focus is on counting out the right number of objects. He is not yet ready to see or deal with smaller numbers that can be combined into larger ones. As Rusty has experiences with number arrangements and sees and hears them described by their parts, he will eventually discover the smaller numbers contained in the larger ones. He will also learn that a single number—six—for example, can be described in a variety of ways, such as *three and three, two and four,* or *six and zero.*

Ms. Lee then sees that Leslie has made several cube arrangements. She stops to talk with Leslie about her work.

"Oh, I see you made a design with three and two and one."

"Yes, I made six with three and two and one," Leslie says. "And here is three and three, and this is three and three and one. And I can make more, too."

Leslie is intrigued with all the ways that she thinks six cubes can be arranged. She is very comfortable describing each design she makes by its parts, and she is focused on the fact that numbers can be described in lots of ways. She does not yet remember the particular combinations. She has not noticed her inconsistency in thinking both that three and three is six and that three and three and one is six. Ms. Lee asks Leslie to recount the cubes in several of her designs, thus allowing her to find and correct her own mistake.

Craig has used buttons to make several arrangements to show six. Ms. Lee asks him to describe his arrangements with numbers. Craig is eager to talk about his work.

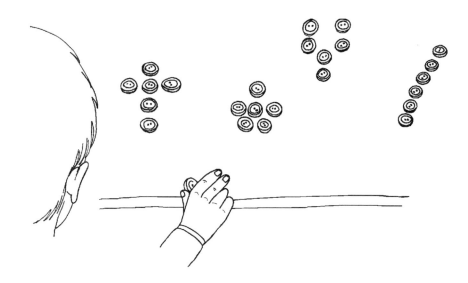

"There's two and three and one, five and one, four and two, six and zero."

"Can you think of any number combinations you haven't made yet?" Ms. Lee asks.

Craig thinks a moment and says, "Oh yeah. I didn't make three and three yet."

Ms. Lee sees that Craig knows the combinations for six. She still feels the activity is appropriate for Craig because of its problem-solving nature. He is challenged by the task of finding *all* the possible ways. However, Ms. Lee believes he is ready to move on to larger numbers, so she suggests that he work with seven when he finishes what he is doing.

Ms. Lee moves back to watch the children who are working with cube trains. They have had quite a while to work and they have accomplished quite a bit. Joseph is busy making trains, but Ms. Lee sees that he is repeating the same two or three trains over and over. She helps him focus on the duplicates that he has made.

"Can you find a train that looks just like this one? Are there more?" After Joseph has found several identical trains, Ms. Lee says, "Now find one that looks different from these." She wants to encourage Joseph to make as many different trains as he can, so she asks, "Can you make another one that looks different from all the others?"

When Joseph looks a little confused, she suggests, "What if you made a train with one yellow? I don't see any like that." Joseph gets to work, making a train with just one yellow and checking to make sure he doesn't have another one just like it.

Ms. Lee notices that Margo is very involved. She has made many arrangements and is searching for more. Ms. Lee does not interrupt Margo while she is so intent. This child is not working to please the teacher—she is working to please herself.

Becky has found numerous combinations for five, but she has not organized them in any way. Ms. Lee remembers that Becky had a hard time thinking of more than three or four arrangements during the first few days that she was assigned this task. She is pleased to see how freely the girl is working now. Ms. Lee knows that Becky must find her own way of organizing her work. However, she asks Becky some questions to help focus her attention on ways that her trains are related.

"Can you find all the ways with one red and the rest white? with two reds? Look, you made two that are opposites—this one has two reds and three whites, and this one looks similar, except it has two whites and three reds. Can you find any more that are opposites?"

Becky becomes intrigued with sorting the trains into groups that are alike in some way and goes back to work, not noticing that Ms. Lee has moved on.

Ms. Lee will have the children work with these same stations tomorrow. Some of the children will continue working with the same manipulatives they chose today. Others will be ready to try a different manipulative. In fact, this same set of stations will be brought out for many more days so that the children will get lots of practice with the combinations in ways that require thinking and creativity.

About the Activities

The activities in this chapter offer many opportunities for children to work with the number combinations to ten and to record those combinations with symbols.

Creating Number Combinations

Children need to be immersed in the activities, experiencing them many times over a period of several weeks. Through the repetition of these tasks, children will learn the number combinations.

The amount of time a child will spend with any particular number varies. A rule of thumb is that children should be confident with the combinations for the numbers four, five, and six, and should have experiences creating and describing number combinations for those numbers, and reading and recording them, before working with the numbers seven, eight, nine, and ten.

Many children will benefit from working with the same number for a week or so. At the end of that time, they should begin exploring the next highest number, even if they still need more work with the first. If they practice with a single number for too long, they tend to stop thinking about the combinations and may start giving automatic responses. Sometimes they continue to give such responses even when a different number is introduced. (That is, a child who has been working on combinations for five may automatically say "two and three," instead of saying "two and four," when working with combinations for six.) Finding combinations for a new number even before all the combinations for another number have been mastered encourages the discovery of number relationships and keeps the children alert.

Some children will need several weeks of working with combinations for four, five, and six. They should spend a few days with one number and then move to a different one for a while. This could mean a week working with five, followed by a few days working with four, then with six, back to four, and so forth.

Other children will need just a few days focusing on each number and then will be ready to begin using symbols to represent the combinations.

Labeling Number Combinations with Symbols

Children who are working with number combinations will usually have had previous experiences with writing addition and subtraction equations. They will use these familiar symbols to record the number arrangements and to keep track of their work.

It is important not to assume that children will automatically make the connection between the number combinations they have been working with and the symbols used to represent them. It is common for children to hear a phrase like "three plus four" and to think only of the symbols $3 + 4$, not the quantities that the symbols represent. To help children make the link between the symbols and what they represent, encourage them to decide what they are going to think about when they hear the numbers.

For example, you might say something like this: "When I say the number sentences, I want you to think of something you could hold in your hand. It could be toothpicks, it could be connecting cubes, or it could be apples." Then go on to give the children a variety of number sentences and have them tell you which objects they were thinking about as they figured out each answer.

Working with Larger Numbers

Do not rush your children to work with the numbers from seven to ten until they are able to deal comfortably and confidently with the numbers to six. Since the larger numbers are composed of the smaller numbers, success with the larger numbers depends a great deal on a firm knowledge of the relationships that apply to numbers to six. Children who have a strong understanding of numbers to six, and who have learned to work easily with the symbols for those numbers, have a better chance of understanding the connection between symbols and the real world. This understanding will carry over to their work with larger numbers.

When children begin working with the larger numbers (seven to ten), the nature of the activities changes. Groups of more than four or five objects are not easily recognized by children at a glance unless they are organized in some fashion (or unless children have learned to organize them mentally). The activities that use "number shapes" assume an important role in the teaching of these larger numbers. Appropriate recommendations for how to change the other activities for use with larger numbers are noted in the activity descriptions. Many of the experiences with the larger numbers can involve problem solving, and the children should proceed easily to using symbols to record their experiences.

Reviewing the Number Combinations

In addition to focusing on the combinations for particular numbers, children need to deal with these same combinations along with those of several other numbers. The teacher-directed activities that emphasize instant recognition of combinations provide opportunities for children to pay attention to the totals rather than to the parts of a number.

This kind of practice can be found in the Instant Recognition of Number Combinations activities (3–2 through 3–5) in Chapter Three.

Teacher-Directed Activities

.... Small-Group Activity

Materials: Connecting cubes, sorted by color

Level 1: **Describing a Number by Its Parts**

Children who need to work with the same number should be seated in a circle. Each child makes a train of the specified number of cubes of one color. On the signal "Snap," children break their trains into two parts and hold one part in each hand behind their back. (On any turn, children may choose not to break their train apart and, instead, may hide the entire train in one hand behind their back—to represent the combination of a number and zero.)

Going around the circle, each child takes a turn showing first what is in one hand and then what is in the other while the rest of the children say the number combination shown. The child showing the cubes should *not* say the combination. This will force the other children to examine the cubes closely to determine the combination formed. For example, the children shown here are working with five cubes.

Three and two.

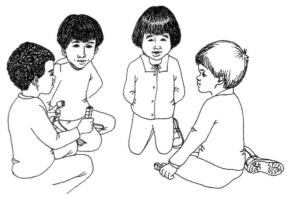

One and four.

When everyone has had a turn, the children put the two parts of their train back together. On the signal "Snap," they break their cubes into different combinations and go around the circle again.

Children repeat the activities several times. The same combinations will appear again and again.

Extension: Working with Numbers Greater Than Six

When working with numbers greater than six, it may be difficult for children to tell at a glance how many cubes are in some of the combinations. Instead of having each child form a combination of her or his choosing, call out the number of cubes you want children to break off their trains. Say, for example:

We are going to work with eight today. Snap together eight cubes. Now break off two.

At your signal, "How many?" the children should say the combination formed. (Avoid asking the question until it appears that each child has determined the combination.)

How many?

Six and two.

Ask the children to put the two parts of their train back together. Then ask them to break off a different number of cubes from the train of eight.

For some lessons, call out the numbers of cubes to be snapped off in random order. For others, call out the numbers in sequence.

Level 2: **Predicting a Missing Part**

This activity proceeds as in Level 1, except that the child showing the cubes keeps one behind his or her back while the other children predict how many cubes are hidden. The child can then reveal the hidden cubes so that the other children can check their predictions.

Materials: Counters, sorted by color · Margarine tubs (1 per child)

Level 1: **Describing a Number by Its Parts**

A small group of children who need to work with the same number should be seated in a circle. Children each take the specified number of counters of one color and place some under their overturned tubs and some on top of their tubs. (Children may choose to put no counters in one place or the other to form the combination of the number and zero.)

The children take turns showing first what is on and then what is under their tubs while the other children say the combinations shown. When everyone has had a turn, children change their arrangement of counters and repeat the activity.

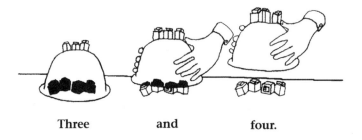

Three   and   four.

Extension: Working with Numbers Greater Than Six

When working with numbers greater than six, it may be difficult for children to tell at a glance how many counters are in some of the combinations. Instead of having each child form a combination of his or her choosing, call out the number of cubes you want children to put under their tubs. Say, for example:

Get seven counters. Put four counters under your tubs. Put the rest on your tubs.

Then ask, "How many?" The children should say the number of counters that is on their tubs and then the number of counters under their tubs. Repeat several times so that children can form a variety of combinations with their counters. For some lessons, call out the numbers of counters in random order. For others, present them in numerical order.

Level 2: **Predicting a Missing Part**

When the children can identify the particular combinations with little or no hesitation, ask them to predict the number of cubes that are under the tubs *before* lifting them. The children then can lift the tubs to check their predictions.

* Based on *Mathematics Their Way,* "Lift the Bowl," p. 181.

Materials: Counters, sorted by color · Blank paper

Announce which number the children are to work with for the day. Then ask them to arrange that number of counters on their papers, from top to bottom, to form an up-and-down (vertical) line. (Children will understand this direction if you tell them to line up the cubes so that they are pointing at their stomachs.) Then they use their hands to make a "wall" that breaks this line. Call out whatever number you want them to "wall off." Say, for example:

Wall off four.

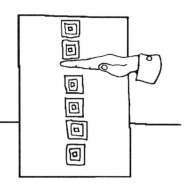

The children make the "wall" so that four counters are closer to them.

Peek over the wall.

The children look over their hands and first say the number of counters *behind* their hands and then say the number of counters that are closer to them. In this example, they would say, "Two and four."

Continue to call out various numbers to be walled off, each time having children say the combinations formed.

* Based on *Mathematics Their Way,* "Peek Through the Wall," p. 183.

Materials: Counters, sorted by color · Working-space papers (1 per child) [BLM #1]

This activity focuses children's attention on the combination of two parts of a number through the process of taking one part away.

Announce which number the children are to work with for the day and have each child put out that number of counters on a working-space paper. At your direction, children should push off the number of counters you specify and then tell how many are left. For example:

Put on six.   *Push off four.*   *How many are left?*

Two.

Variation: Have each child take a turn pushing off some of the counters. Then have the rest of the children tell how many counters were removed and how many are left. For example, as one child performs the action, the other children describe it.

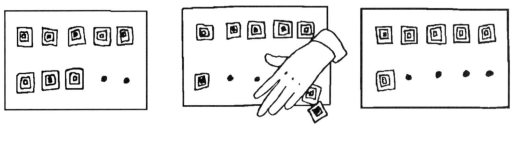

Eight.   Push off two.   Leaves six.

.... **Small-Group Activity**

Materials: Counters, sorted by color · Blank paper

Announce which number the children are to work with for the day and ask them to arrange that number of counters across their papers to form a side-to-side (horizontal) line. (To describe this arrangement further, ask children to line up their counters the way their arms go when they stretch them out to their sides.)

Tell children to place their right hand on the paper to form a "cave." (Display a right-hand outline for those who need help in identifying their right hand.)

Tell children the number of counters to move away from the others and "hide" in the caves. Then, on the cue "How many?" children tell the number of counters *outside* the caves and the number of counters hidden *inside* the caves. On the cue, "Check," they lift their "hand caves" and again say the combination formed.

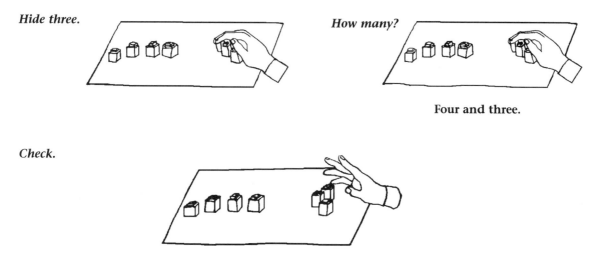

Hide three.

How many?

Four and three.

Check.

Four and three.

Continue to call out various numbers of counters for children to hide, having them continue to identify the combinations formed.

Variation: Children take turns hiding a few of their counters inside their caves. The child who has hidden some counters asks, "How many?" The rest of the children tell the number of counters outside the cave and then determine the hidden part.

* Based on *Mathematics Their Way,* "The Cave," p. 192.

Materials: Counters, sorted by color · Paper bag

Tell the children which number they are to work with for the day and place that number of counters into a paper bag. Have the children take turns reaching into the bag, grabbing some counters and taking them out. The child whose turn it is shows how many he or she took out, and the rest of the group tells how many they think are left in the bag. Then all the counters are dumped from the bag and the guesses are checked. For example:

The number for the day is eight.

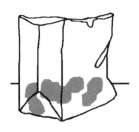
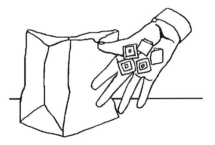

Eight.   Take away five.

How many do you think are still in the bag?

> Three.
> Maybe four.

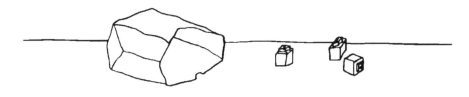

Three are left.

Let's say what happened.

> Eight take away five is three.

See activity 3–22 for a description of Grab-Bag Subtraction Station as an independent activity.

Materials: Unifix Cubes, sorted by color

Have the children sit in a circle. Once you identify the number the children are going to work with for the day, have them take that many cubes and place some on the fingers of one hand and some on the fingers of the other hand. The children take turns showing first one hand and then the other while the rest of the group says the number combination shown. Repeat several times. For example, these combinations could be shown when children are working with the number six.

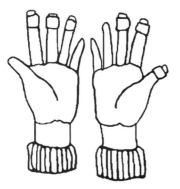

Three and three.

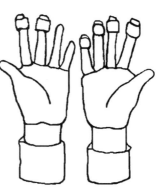

Two and four.

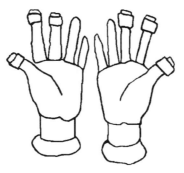

Three and three.

Have we found all the ways to show six?

Allow the children to experience this activity with numbers greater than six, but let them discover on their own which combinations will fit on the fingers of two hands and which will not.

About the Number Shapes

The Number shapes [BLMs #76–82] are distinctive arrangements of squares representing the numbers from four through ten.

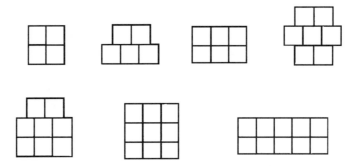

These shapes can be filled with manipulatives in various ways to show number combinations. The shapes have many helpful features.

The arrangement of squares in a shape aid in the recognition of larger numbers. (Squares representing numbers greater than four and five are not easy for children to recognize without counting unless they are organized in some way.)

The shapes also provide specific images for children to picture in their minds, which helps when children are learning to visualize objects that are not present.

Finally, the number shapes help establish children's understanding of the relationship between addition and subtraction. Children who know that two plus three equals five do not automatically know that five take away three equals two because they do not see how these processes are related. They seem to think about addition and subtraction as two totally different experiences. In most situations in which children subtract, the number they started with disappears once they have taken a quantity away. This seems to contribute to the problem young children have with relating the addition facts to the subtraction facts. For example:

Start with six.   *Take away two.*

Once having taken away the two, the six has disappeared and can't be referred to again unless the child is able to reverse his or her thought process and imagine the counters back together again.

This ability to reverse one's thinking does not develop for most children until at least age seven. Many children will represent the above situation by saying or writing $4 - 2 = 4$ rather than $6 - 2 = 4$ because they've lost track of how many they started with.

Using the number shapes for both addition and subtraction gives children the opportunity to discover that the combinations of smaller numbers that make up any particular number are the same combinations that are involved when they are taking that number apart. Thus, when the problem $6 - 2 = 4$ is modeled on the number shape, the shape serves to remind the children that they started with 6. Also, because the empty spaces remain after the counters are removed, the shape shows 6 as it relates to the 2 and the 4.

2–8 Working with Number Shapes .... Small-Group Activity

Materials: Counters, sorted by color • Number shapes for the number of the day (1 per child) [BLMs #76–82]

Give each child in the group the same size number shape. Direct the children to perform a series of actions with the shape. The following examples use the "six" shape; however, you can adapt the same actions to any of the shapes.

It is important to use the shapes for both addition and subtraction from the very beginning so that the children learn to deal with the shapes flexibly. For addition, have children use counters of two colors to highlight the two parts of the number. For subtraction, have children use counters of one color to emphasize the whole number. Present a variety of directions during one lesson. Say, for example:

Put three red and three blue counters on your shape. This shows that three and three equals six.

Clear off your shape. Now put four red counters and two blue counters on your shape. Who can tell me what that shows?

Four plus two equals six.

NOTE: Children may describe the action in a variety of ways, such as "four and two is six" or "four and two more is six altogether." Accept any expression that accurately reflects the situation.

Put two red counters on your shape. Fill the rest of the shape with blue counters. What do you have?

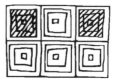

Two plus four equals six.

Can you find another way to arrange those counters on your shape? How did you arrange them?

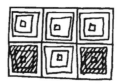

I put two red ones on the bottom corners and the rest blue.

Can you find another way? How did you arrange them this time?

I put two red ones in the middle and the rest blue.

NOTE: Seeing two and four positioned in a multitude of ways helps children think flexibly as they internalize the number relationships.

Fill up your shape with blue counters. Take one off. Who can tell what we did?

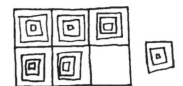

Six minus one is five.

For a related independent activity, see Number-Shape Arrangements (activity 2–19) Level 1.

Materials: Counters, sorted by color • Number shapes for the number of the day (1 per child) [BLMs #76–82] • Number cubes (See preparation below.)
Preparation: You will need three number cubes: one with the numerals 0–4, one with 1–6, and one with 4–9. Use the 0–4 cube for the four and five number shapes; use either the 0–4 or the 1–6 cube for the six, seven, and eight number shapes; and use any of the three number cubes for the nine and ten number shapes. (See Materials Preparation on page 14 for making, color coding, and using number cubes.)

Rolling a number cube to determine the number combinations to be made is highly motivating for children and leads them to create a variety of combinations for each number shape. The following examples use the "six" shape. The same activities can be adapted to any of the other shapes.

Addition

Have the children take turns rolling a number cube to see how many counters they are to place on their number shapes. For each roll, they place that number of counters of one color on the shape and fill in the remaining spaces with counters of a different color. Then they describe the number combination formed.

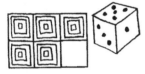

I rolled five.

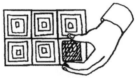

I need one more.

Five plus one is six.

Subtraction

The children fill the number shapes with counters of one color. One child rolls a number cube to see how many to take away and describes the action with numbers.

I rolled four.

Six minus four equals two.

For a related independent activity, see Number Shapes: Using Number Cubes (activity 2–20) Level 1.

About the Number Trains

The Number-train outlines [BLMs #91–98] are sized so that when connecting cubes are snapped together, they fit into the outlines exactly.

The numbers represented by the train outlines are not as instantly recognizable to children as they are in the number-shape arrangements. The outlines do, however, provide children with an alternative way to experience the number facts and number relationships.

As with the number shapes, it is important that the children use the number-train outlines in a variety of ways from the very start so that they learn to deal with them flexibly. Just as you did with the number shapes, use counters of two colors when you want to focus on addition, and counters of one color when you want to focus on subtraction.

2–10 Working with Number Trains

Small-Group Activity

Materials: Connecting cubes, sorted by color · Number-train outlines for the number of the day (1 per child) [BLMs #91–98]

Give the children a variety of directions for filling their number-train outlines. Include work with adding, subtracting, and comparing numbers. In the following examples, the children are working with a seven-train outline. The same activities can be adapted for train outlines of other lengths.

Addition

Using the green and yellow cubes, snap together enough to fill in your number-train outline. How many did you need?   Seven.

Hold up one of the children's trains.

How many green cubes did Janelle use?   Four.

How many yellow cubes did Janelle use?   Three.

Yes, four and three is seven.

Hold up other children's trains and have the group read the number combination shown by each. Ask children to consistently read the number of one color first, then the other color; in this case, first green and then yellow.

Subtraction

Now fill your outline with green cubes. Take away four cubes. How many are left?

Three.

Yes, seven take away four is three.

Repeat the activity, each time asking the children to take away a different number from seven and then to describe what they did.

Missing Part

Put three cubes on your outline. How many more cubes do you need to completely fill the outline?

Four.

Repeat, varying the starting numbers.

Describing Combinations

Hold up a two-color train, with cubes of one color separated into two groups. Show the children that the train can be described in two ways.

How many yellow cubes?

Four.

How many green cubes?

Three.

How many altogether?

Three plus four equals seven.

We can describe this train another way, too. We can also say "One plus four plus two equals seven."

Have the children take turns making and holding up different number trains so that the others can describe them by the arrangement of the number of cubes of each color.

Comparing Numbers

Fill your outline with yellow cubes. Make a green train three cubes long and line it up with one end of your yellow train. How many more green cubes do you need to make your green train as long as your yellow train?

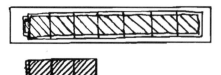

Repeat, varying the length of the yellow train.

Learning the Combinations

Show me one plus six with your cubes. Can you make one plus six a different way? Can you make it still another way?

Repeat, varying the combinations.

Variation: After you or a child performs a particular action, have the children describe what was done. For example:

Snap seven cubes together and put them on a train outline. Break off four.

Use number words to tell me what I did.

Seven minus four equals three, or seven take away four leaves three.

A child named Sean puts two blue cubes on the seven-train outline and then puts five red cubes on the outline.

Use number words to tell me what Sean did.

Two plus five equals seven.

Materials: Connecting cubes, sorted by color · Number-train outlines for the number of the day (1 per child) [BLMs #91–98] · Number cubes (See preparation below.)
Preparation: You will need three number cubes: one with the numerals 0–4, one with 1–6, and one with 4–9. Use the 0–4 cube for the four and five number trains; use either the 0–4 or the 1–6 cube for the six, seven, and eight number trains; and use any of the three number cubes for the nine and ten number shapes. (See additional notes on making, color coding, and using number cubes in Materials Preparation, p. 14.)

The following examples are based on the six- and seven-train outlines. The same activities can be adapted for train outlines of other lengths.

Addition

Have the children take turns rolling a number cube to see how many cubes they are to place on their number-train outlines. They place that number of cubes of one color on the outlines and fill in the remaining spaces with cubes of a different color. Then they describe the number combinations formed.

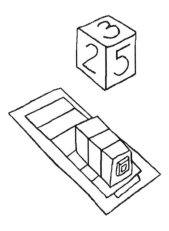
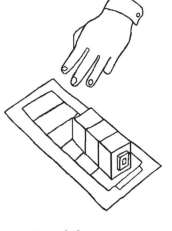
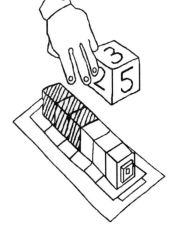

| I rolled three. | I need three more. | Three and three is six. |

Subtraction

The children start by filling their number-train outlines with cubes of one color. One child rolls a number cube to see how many to take away and then describes the action with numbers.

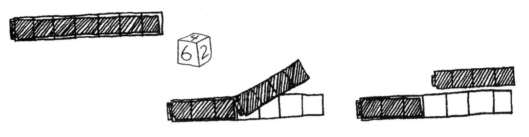

We need to break off four.

Seven minus four equals three.

NOTE: Encourage the children to break off the cubes as small trains, rather than as individual units. Thus, to take away four:

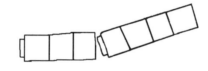

This way.

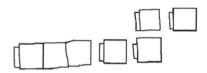

Not this way.

Materials: Counters, sorted by color · Identical counting boards (1 per child)
[BLMs #2–6]

Give each child one counting board. The following examples show the ocean setting, but any of the settings can be used. After you have identified the number of
the day, have the children take that number of counters and decide individually
which people, animals, or objects they want the counters to represent.

The children take turns telling a story to demonstrate a number combination that
matches the total number of counters. For example, when six is the number of the
day. Children might tell stories like these.

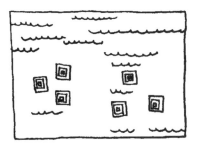

Three fish were swimming.
Three more came. That
makes six fish swimming.

Six ships were sailing on the
water. Two sank and then
there were four left.

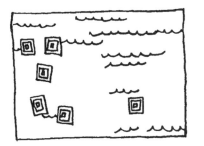

Five fish were in the water.
One more fish came. Then
there were six fish.

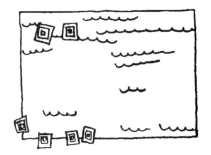

Six kids were swimming in
the ocean. Four kids got cold
and went home. Only two
kids stayed longer.

*For a related independent activity, see Counting Boards: Making Up Number-Combination
Stories (activity 2–18).*

Materials: As specified for the individual activities described previously. (See activity references below.)

Children who are working with number combinations will usually have had previous experiences writing addition and subtraction equations. They will use these familiar symbols to record the number arrangements and to keep track of their work.

If you need to introduce the recording of number combinations with symbols, plan to do so in three stages as you present some of the familiar activities described earlier, such as Snap It, The Tub Game, The Wall Game, The Cave Game, and Working with Number Shapes. At first, model the writing of the equations, recording them on the board as the children report them. Challenge the children to look for all possible combinations as they work with the activities.

Then, when the children are ready to write the number combinations, provide them with individual chalkboards. Continue to have them search for various ways to make the combinations. After you write the combinations that children report to you, have them copy what you have written.

As a final stage, have the children write the number combinations themselves as they report them. After the children have finished writing, write each equation on the board so that they can check their work.

Present each game in a problem-solving context by posing a question, as shown in the following examples.

Snap It (See activity 2–1.)

Today we are going to use six cubes to make a train. We want to find all the ways we can break our train in two parts. Remember, it's OK to break off zero cubes. Who knows a way we can break our train in two?

As the children report the ways they find, record each equation on the chalkboard. For example:

I broke my train, so I have one and five.

This is how we write what you did. One and five equals six.

Continue to write the ways that the children report what they have found. Each time they report a combination, they should look to see if it has already been written on the chalkboard.

I made three and three. Oh, I see it. It's already on the board.

The Tub Game (See activity 2–2.)

Today we are going to work with six cubes. We want to find out how many different ways we can put some of our cubes on top of our tub and some of our cubes under our tub. Who can find one way?

$$\begin{array}{r} 3 \\ +3 \\ \hline 6 \end{array}$$

The Wall Game (See activity 2–3.)

Use your hands to make a "wall" that breaks your line of six counters. How many different ways can we make walls to break this line? Yes, one way is five and one.

$$\begin{array}{r} 5 \\ +1 \\ \hline 6 \end{array}$$

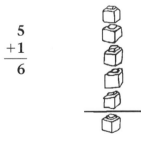

The Cave Game (See activity 2–5.)

We have six cubes altogether to hide in our hand caves. How many different ways can we hide these cubes in our caves?

$$4 + 2 = 6$$

Working with the Number Shapes (See activities 2–8 and 2–9.)

How many different ways can we put red and green cubes on our "six" number shapes?

$$2 + 2 + 2 = 6$$

After having spent many days searching for all the ways to make a number as they do the various activities, some children will be able to predict the ways that they will find. They may approach the task in an organized manner and eventually find the pattern for all the possible ways. Allow the children to do this in their own time. You can help them focus on what is happening by posing questions like these:

How many ways did we find to make six? Do you think we've found all the ways?

How many ways did we find to make five?

Can you predict the number of ways we will find to make seven?

See How Many Ways? (2–25) for an extension of this activity and The Snap-It Station (3–25) for ways to use Snap It as an independent activity.

Independent Activities

About the Number Arrangements*

The next four activities engage children in making arrangements (or "designs") that demonstrate all the combinations for a given number. The children should spend several days or weeks at the first level creating and describing arrangements using a variety of materials. Later, they should label the parts of their number arrangements with addition cards or by writing equations.

The activities can sometimes involve recording the arrangements. You will need some of the children's recordings for use in the teacher-directed activity Instant Recognition of Number Arrangements (activity 3–2). Plan to save a variety of recordings of each number.

Be aware that the record-making process can hamper a child's creativity and productivity. Be sure to provide children with many opportunities to explore problems using manipulatives alone without having to record their work. You may want to have the children make arrangements for a certain period of time and then record just a few of them.

TIP: *When a Child Needs a More Specific Assignment*

Open-ended tasks like the number arrangements activities, when assigned as independent work, have both advantages and disadvantages. One advantage is that when the assignment is to "do as many as you can," no child can finish early and so needs an additional task. Because such an assignment sets no limits, some children will accomplish much beyond what you might have assigned if you had established a specific amount to do. The disadvantage is, however, that other children will accomplish much less than you might have assigned because they feel no pressure to complete a particular amount.

Therefore, assign a certain amount only to those children who need a specific assignment. This can be done by providing the child with a "workboard" to be filled in, thus defining a specific amount to be accomplished.

The workboard can be made from a 12" × 18" sheet of paper folded into eight sections. The child is to put one arrangement into each section, and thus will have to complete eight arrangements in order to finish the task.

* Based on *Mathematics Their Way*, "The Number Stations," p. 168.

Materials: *Level 1:* Connecting cubes or wooden cubes
Extension: Same as for Level 1, plus 6" × 9" pieces of paper ▪ 1" squares of colored paper ▪ Glue
Level 2: Same as for Level 1, plus Addition cards [BLMs #64–68] ▪ 2" × 6" strips of paper

Level 1: Finding Combinations

The children create a variety of arrangements for the number they are working with that day.

Occasionally ask the children to use number words to describe their arrangements. A single arrangement can be described in a variety of ways. For example:

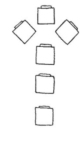

One and two and three.

Four and two.

Three plus three.

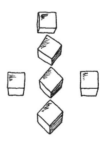

Three and three.

One and three and two.

Four plus two.

Variation: Increase the level of difficulty for those children who are ready by posing questions like these:

How can you arrange cubes so that their full sides are touching?

What designs can you make that have corners "kissing"?

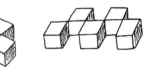

Can you make a square with your number?

| **It works for four.** | **I can make a square with nine.** | **I can't make a square with five cubes.** |

Extension: Making Recordings

Have the children record some of their arrangements on 6" × 9" pieces of paper, gluing down small squares of paper to show the way they have arranged the cubes.

Level 2: Reading and Writing Equations

After having many experiences creating and describing arrangements, children should begin to label the parts of their number arrangements with symbols. They can do this by using addition cards or by writing their own equations on 2" × 6" strips of paper. For example:

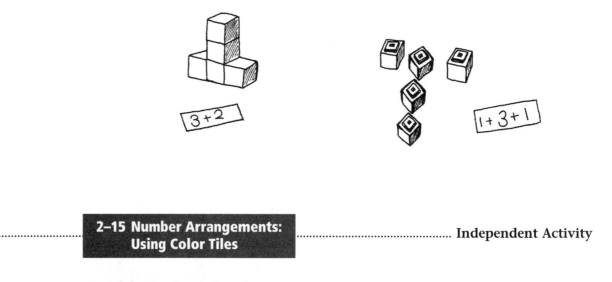

2–15 Number Arrangements: Using Color Tiles

Materials: *Level 1:* Color Tiles
Extension: Same as for Level 1, plus 6" × 9" pieces of paper ▪ 1" squares of colored paper ▪ Glue
Level 2: Same as for Level 1, plus Addition cards [BLMs #64–68] ▪ 2" × 6" strips of paper

Level 1: Finding Combinations

The children use Color Tiles to create a variety of arrangements for their number of the day. For example:

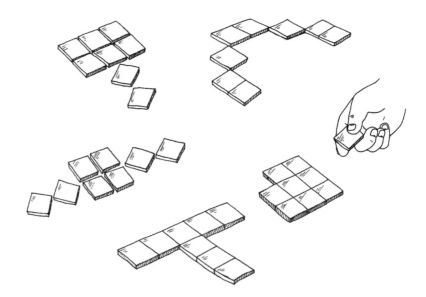

Occasionally ask the children to use number words to describe their arrangements to you or to an adult assistant. For example:

Two and four.

Three and three.

Five and one.

Extension: Making Recordings

Have the children glue down small squares of paper on 6" × 9" pieces of paper to record their tile arrangements.

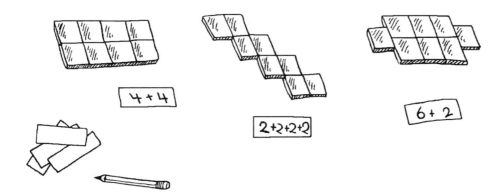

Level 2: Reading and Writing Equations

After having many experiences creating and describing arrangements, children should begin to label the parts of their number arrangements with symbols, either by using addition cards or by writing their own equations on 2" × 6" strips of paper.

Materials: *Level 1:* Toothpicks
Extension: Same as for Level 1, plus 6" × 9" pieces of paper · Glue
Level 2: Same as for Level 1, plus Addition cards [BLMs #64–68] · 2" × 6" strips
of paper

Level 1: **Finding Combinations**

The children use toothpicks to create a variety of arrangements for their number of
the day.

Sometimes, ask the children to use number
words to describe their arrangements to you
or to an adult assistant. For example:

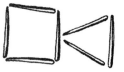

Four and three.
Three and one and three.

Variation: To raise the level of difficulty, suggest that children make more challenging arrangements.

How many designs can you make with your toothpicks touching end to end?

How many designs can you make that have square corners (right angles)?

Extension: Making Recordings

Have the children make recordings by gluing toothpicks onto 6" × 9" pieces of paper to match their toothpick arrangements.

Level 2: **Reading and Writing Equations**

After having many experiences creating and describing arrangements, children should begin to label the parts of their number arrangements with symbols, either by using addition cards or by writing their own equations on 2" × 6" strips of paper.

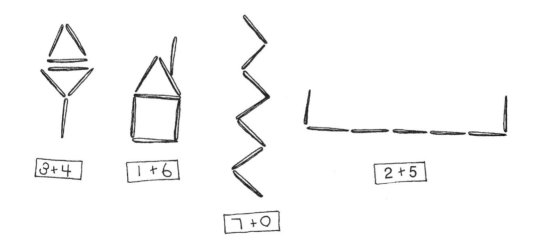

Materials: *Level 1:* Collections
Extension: Same as for Level 1, plus 6" × 9" pieces of paper • Glue
Level 2: Same as for Level 1, plus Addition cards [BLMs #64–68] • 2" × 6" strips
of paper

Level 1: Finding Combinations

The children use any collections available to create a variety of arrangements for
their number of the day. When the children are making arrangements from collections, any one arrangement should be made from one single type of collection.

Occasionally ask the children to use number words to describe their arrangements.
For example:

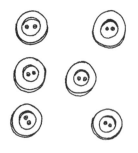

Three and one and two.

Three and three.

Four and one and one.

Extension: Making Recordings

Have the children make records on 6" × 9" pieces of paper, using crayons to draw symbols to show their arrangements.

Level 2: **Reading and Writing Equations**

After having many experiences creating and describing arrangements, children should begin to label the parts of their number arrangements with symbols, either by using addition cards or by writing their own equations on 2" × 6" strips of paper.

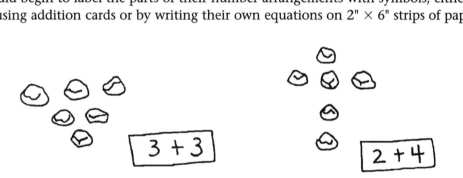

Materials: *Level 1:* Counters, sorted by color · Counting boards (a set of 8 of the same board per child) [BLMs #2–6]
Level 2: Same as for Level 1, plus Addition cards [BLMs #64–68] · 2" × 6" strips of paper

Level 1: **Finding Combinations**

Have each child spread out eight counting boards. The child should use two colors of counters on each board to model a number-combination story for the number of the day. On occasion have children share their stories with one another. For example:

This one shows that there was one red bird in the tree. Six blue birds flew there, too. Then there were seven birds in all.

Variation: Children draw addition cards to determine which combinations to show on the counting boards.

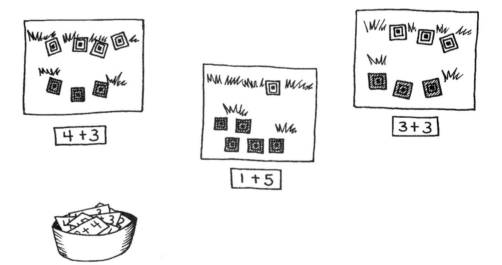

Level 2: **Reading and Writing Equations**

After having many experiences organizing number combinations on the counting boards, children should begin to label their combinations with symbols, either by using addition cards or by writing their own equations on 2" × 6" strips of paper.

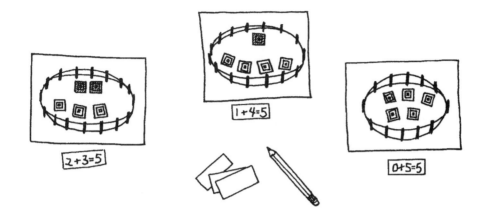

For a related teacher-directed activity, see Counting Boards: Number-Combination Stories (activity 2–12).

2–19 Number-Shape Arrangements .... Independent Activity

Materials: *Level 1:* Connecting cubes or Color Tiles (in two colors) • Number Shapes cards (enough to give each child 8 to 10 shapes for the number of the day) [BLMs #76–82]
Variation: Same as for Level 1, plus Addition cards [BLMs #64–68]
Extension: Same as for Level 1, plus crayons • Number Shapes Recording Sheets [BLMs #83–89]
Level 2: Same as for Level 1, plus crayons and pencil for each child
Preparation: Run off BLMs #76–82 on tagboard and cut apart to make number shapes cards.

Level 1: **Finding Combinations**

Using the number shapes cards for the number of the day, the children arrange counters of two colors to make different combinations.

Children can create their own combinations or draw from a pool of addition cards to determine which combinations to build on the number shapes.

Extension: Making Recordings

To record their work, the children can color the worksheets to match their arrangements. The large number shapes worksheets can be used in two ways. They can be cut apart so that the children can take as many as they are able to do, or children can each complete one whole worksheet. Some children may be ready to use the small number shapes worksheets.

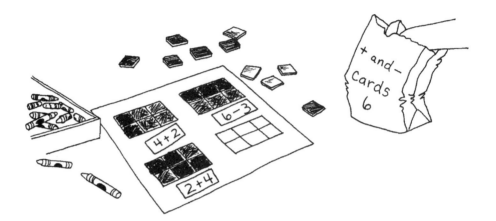

Level 2: **Writing Equations**

After the children have created and colored combinations on the number shapes worksheets, they write equations to describe their combinations.

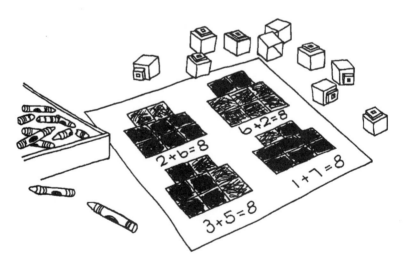

Materials: Counters, sorted by color • Number Shapes cards [BLMs #76–82] •
Number Shapes reproduced as worksheets (1 sheet per child) [BLMs #76–82] or
Number Shapes Recording Sheets [BLMs #83–89] • Crayons • Number cubes
(1 per child)

Preparation: You need to make sure that children have access to the appropriate
number cube, depending on the numbers that they need to work with. They will
need the 0–4 cube for the four and five number shapes; either the 0–4 or the 1–6
cube for the six, seven, and eight number shapes; and the 0–4, 1–6, or 4–9 number
cube for the nine and ten number shapes. (See Materials Preparation on page 14 for
making, color coding, and using number cubes.)

Level 1: **Finding Combinations**

The children work with the number shapes cards for the number of the day. They roll
their number cubes to determine how many counters to put on or take off the shape.

Addition

The child rolls the number cube to
determine how many counters of a
first color to place on the number
shape. After placing those, the child
fills in the remaining spaces with
counters of a second color and then
records this arrangement by coloring
a number shape on a worksheet to
match it. The child continues in this
way until the worksheet is filled in.

Subtraction

The child starts by filling the number
shapes card with counters of one
color and then rolls the number cube
to determine how many counters to
take off. After taking away the indicated number of counters, the child
colors a number shape on the worksheet to record how many are left.

Level 2: **Writing Equations**

After completing their worksheet recordings, the children write the equations to describe each of the combinations.

Addition

Subtraction

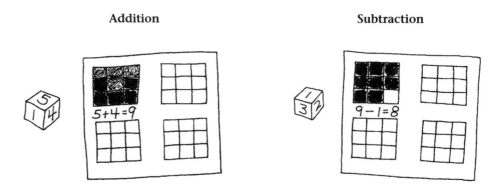

2–21 Number Shapes: Using Spinners

.... **Independent Activity**

Materials: Counters, sorted by color · Number Shapes cards for the number of the day (1 per child) [BLMs #76–82] · Number Shapes Equations worksheets (1 per child) [BLM #90] · Plus-or-Minus Spinners (1 per child) · Number cubes (1 per child)
Preparation: You need to make sure that children have access to the appropriate number cube, depending on the numbers that they need to work with. They will need the 0–4 cube for the four and five number shapes; either the 0–4 or the 1–6 cube for the six, seven, and eight number shapes; and the 0–4, 1–6, or 4–9 number cube for the nine and ten number shapes. (See Materials Preparation on page 14 for making, color coding, and using number cubes.)

The children each get a number shapes card for their number of the day. They circle the matching shape on their Number Shapes Equations worksheet.

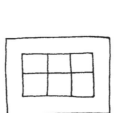

Developing Number Concepts   Addition and Subtraction

The child spins the spinner to determine whether to add or subtract. If the spinner lands on *plus*, the child rolls the number cube to determine how many counters of a first color to place on the number shape. After placing those, the child then fills in the rest of the shape using counters of a second color and records the corresponding equation on the worksheet.

If the spinner lands on *minus*, the child fills the number shapes card with counters of one color, rolls the number cube to determine how many counters to take off, and records the corresponding equation on the worksheet.

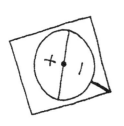
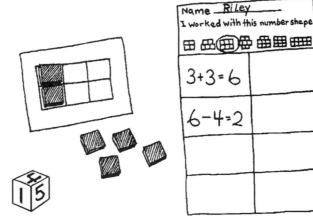

Materials: *Level 1:* Counting cubes, sorted by color
Extension: Same as for Level 1, plus Number-Train Outlines worksheet for the number of the day (1 per child) [BLMs #91–98] and, for those children who are ready, Number Trains Recording Sheets [BLMs #99–106] • Crayons
Level 2: Same as for Level 1 Extension.

Level 1: Finding Combinations

The children snap together as many different combinations of cubes of two colors as they can to represent their number of the day.

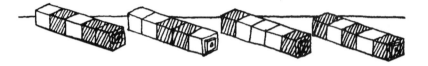

Extension: Making Recordings

Have the children make records of their work by coloring number-train outlines to match the cube trains they have created.

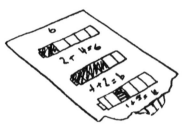

Level 2: Writing Equations

After children have created trains of different arrangements and have colored the worksheets to record them, they write equations to describe the combinations. This can be done either on a whole sheet of number-train outlines or on individual outlines cut from the sheet. If using individual outlines, the children complete as many as they can and staple their papers to form small books.

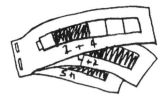

NOTE: It is suggested that the number-train outlines be cut apart. Although you do not have to do this, there are some advantages to doing so. Using individual number-train outlines, the children complete as many as they can rather than an assigned number. Thus, some children will be able to complete many more than you may have assigned, while other children will not be frustrated with an assignment they can't complete.

2–23 Number Trains: Using Number Cubes

.... **Independent Activity**

Materials: *Level 1:* Connecting cubes, sorted by color · Number-Train Outlines [BLMs #91–98] · Number-Train Outlines reproduced as worksheets (1 per child) [BLMs #91–98] · Number Trains Recording Sheets [BLMs #99–106] · Crayons · Number cubes (1 per child)]
Level 2: Same as for Level 1, plus pencils
Preparation: Run off BLMs #91–98 on tagboard. Cut apart to make the number-trains outlines. You need to make sure that children have access to the appropriate number cube, depending on the numbers that they need to work with. They will need the 0–4 cube for the four and five number shapes; either the 0–4 or the 1–6 cube for the six, seven, and eight number shapes; and the 0–4, 1–6, or 4–9 number cube for the nine and ten number shapes. (See Materials Preparation on page 14 for making, color coding, and using number cubes.)

Level 1: Finding Combinations

The children each get a number-train outline for their number of the day. They roll a number cube to determine how many cubes to add or to subtract.

Addition

The child rolls the number cube to determine how many cubes of a first color to place on the number-train outline. After placing these, the child fills in the rest of the outline with cubes of a second color and records this arrangement by coloring a worksheet outline.

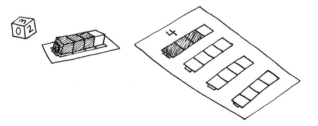

Subtraction

The child starts by filling the number-train outline with cubes of one color and then rolls the number cube to determine how many cubes to take away. After taking away the indicated number of cubes, the child colors a worksheet outline to record how many are left.

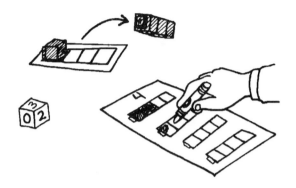

Level 2: Writing Equations

After completing their worksheet recordings, the children write the corresponding equation for each train.

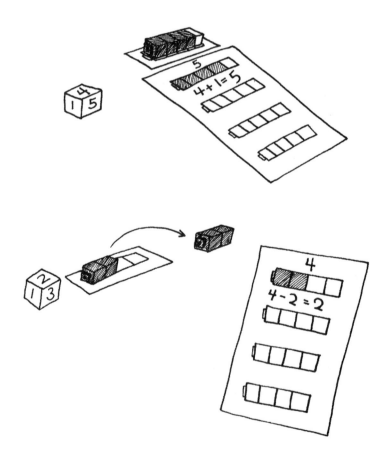

Materials: Connecting cubes, sorted by color • Number-Train Outlines for the number of the day (1 per child) [BLMs #91–98] • Number Trains Equations Worksheets (1 per child) [BLM #107] • Plus-or-Minus Spinners (1 per child) • Number cubes (1 per child)

Preparation: You need to make sure that children have access to the appropriate number cube, depending on the numbers that they need to work with. They will need the 0–4 cube for the four and five number trains; either the 0–4 or the 1–6 cube for the six, seven, and eight number trains; and the 0–4, 1–6, or 4–9 number cube for the nine and ten number trains. (See Materials Preparation on page 14 for making, color coding, and using number cubes.)

The children each get a number-train outline for the number of the day. They circle the matching train outline on their Number Trains Equations worksheet.

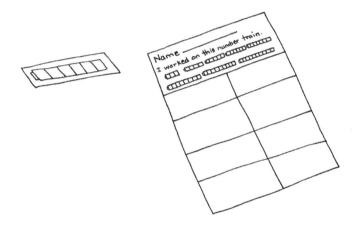

The child spins the spinner to determine whether to add or subtract. If the spinner lands on *plus,* the child rolls the number cube to find how many cubes of a first color to place on the train outline. After placing these, the child then fills in the rest of the outline using cubes of a second color and records the corresponding equation in one box on the worksheet.

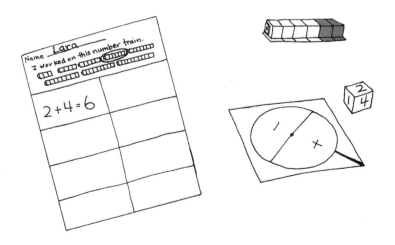

If the spinner lands on *minus*, the child fills the number-train outline with cubes of one color, rolls the number cube to determine how many cubes to take off and then records the corresponding equation on the worksheet.

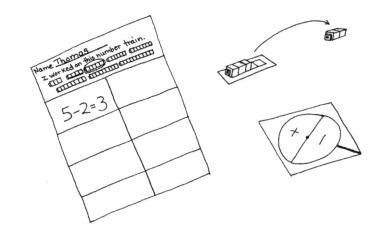

2-25 How Many Ways?

Independent Activity

Materials: Equations Worksheets (1 per child) [BLM #108] • Counters and other items specified for the individual games, described elsewhere (See activity numbers below.)

After the children have experienced the activities for learning the number combinations in teacher-directed small groups, they can repeat the work independently, using different numbers. The following teacher-directed activities can be used in this way:

- Snap It (2–1)
- The Tub Game (2–2)
- The Wall Game (2–3)

- The Cave Game (2–5)
- Working with Number Shapes (2–8)
- Working with Number Trains (2–10)

To do any of these activities independently, the children search for all possible combinations for the number they are working with. They record all the combinations they find on the Equations worksheet. For example:

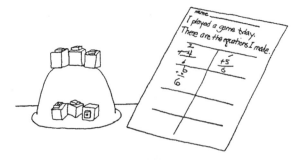

I found another way. Three on top and three underneath. That is three plus three.

Materials: Connecting cubes, sorted by color · Butcher-paper graph · Number-Train Outlines for the number of the day reproduced as worksheets [BLMs #91–98] · Crayons, scissors, glue

Preparation: On a length of butcher paper, set up a graph with columns for every possible combination for the number of the day. You can label the columns with the possible combinations or leave this for the children to do. Duplicate BLMs #91–98 to provide a supply of number-train outline worksheets. Either cut apart the individual trains or provide scissors for the children to cut them apart.

This is a good follow-up activity to the children's independent work with Number-Train Arrangements (2–22), Number Trains: Using Number Cubes (2–23), and Number Trains: Using Spinners (2–24). The children should have had many experiences working with number trains before you ask them to make this graph.

If children have had the appropriate experience, a small group can work together on this activity without your direct involvement. Start them off by identifying the number they are to work with. The children should try to find all the possible number-train arrangements for the combinations that make up that number.

For each new arrangement they find, the children color a number-train outline and place it in the appropriate column of the butcher-paper graph.

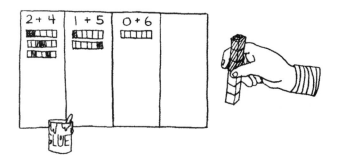

Three plus three is not up there. I can start a new column.

I have a different way to
make one plus five.

Oh, one like this is already up.
I can't use this one.

Materials: Counters, sorted by color · 18" × 24" newsprint folded into 8 sections, or 12" × 18" newsprint folded into 4 sections (1 sheet per child)

This activity can be used as an extension for the Number Arrangements experiences (activities 2–14 through 2–17). It works equally well as an independent work-station activity or a whole-class activity.

Each child gets a sheet of newsprint folded either into four or eight sections to use as a working space. The children choose one type of counter and build a different design to represent an assigned number in each section of their paper. Then they write a number sentence to describe each design.

When the children have finished, they remove the counters from their papers. After re-reading the number combinations, they rebuild designs to match them, this time using a different type of counter.

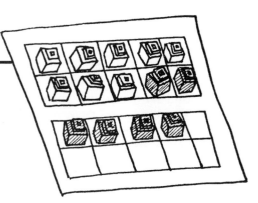

3

**When textbook or
curriculum objectives are:**

- Basic addition or subtraction
  facts to 20

  - Adding and subtracting
    (horizontally and vertically)

    - Using strategies to solve addition
      and subtraction problems

Then you want to teach

Developing Strategies for Adding and Subtracting

Developing Strategies for Adding and Subtracting

When children are focused on completing an addition or subtraction problem, they often count to get an answer and then write down that answer without paying attention to it. They may count without thinking about number relationships or what they know about numbers. The activities in this chapter provide children with ongoing experiences that will help them move past automatically counting and on to developing and applying strategies based on number relationships.

A child's level of proficiency in applying strategies to solve problems depends in large part on his or her facility with number. For example, the following problem may be answered in one of several ways, depending on the child's ability to work with numbers.

"How many tiles in the design?"

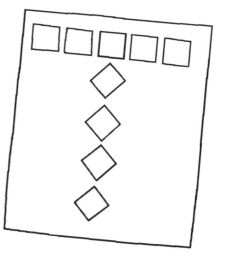

- *A child could answer by counting all.* Allie is very methodical as she solves the problem. She carefully counts each of the tiles. "One, two, three, four, five, six, seven, eight, nine."
- *A child could answer by counting on.* Nick doesn't need to count them all. He counts on, saying, "This is five, so it's six, seven, eight, nine. There are nine tiles."
- *A child could answer by seeing relationships.* Tara says, "I think there are nine, because five and five are ten, and if you take one off, that makes nine." She then counts them all to see if she was right.
- *A child could answer by knowing the number combination.* Jesse simply says, "Nine. Five and four make nine."

The most natural way for young children to determine "How many?" is to count *all* the objects. Children must be allowed to use this strategy as long as they need to. In fact, they *must* count if they have not yet learned the number relationships needed for more sophisticated methods. At an early stage of development, getting out the correct number of counters and counting them accurately is challenge enough.

The problem is not that children count but rather that many of them do not move beyond counting. Our role is to help children notice, understand, and internalize number relationships. We can do this by providing them with appropriate experiences and by helping them discover that number relationships can be used to solve problems.

Children do not develop more and more sophisticated ways of solving problems quickly. It is essential that we give them time to develop proficiency with numbers to ten before expecting them to see the relationships among numbers greater than ten. While children can work with problems dealing with numbers much greater than ten, they will most likely need to solve these problems by counting. Through their work with smaller numbers, children build the strategies that they can then apply to their work with larger numbers.

Our job is not to teach children to use particular strategies. If we attempt to teach children to use strategies before they themselves see the need for them, they will either not use them, or they will use them inappropriately or without understanding. Our job is to provide situations in which children have opportunities to see various ways of solving problems and to recognize the value of the strategies for themselves. We want children to take on these ideas when they make sense to them and to use strategies only as they become useful and meaningful to them.

Goals for Children's Learning*

Goals

Given a variety of problem situations, children will:

- Solve addition and subtraction problems with increasing confidence, flexibility, and efficiency

- Apply increasingly sophisticated strategies

- Describe how they solved the problems

- Eventually internalize number combinations to the point at which they know the sums and differences without having to figure them out

* Adapted from *How Do We Know They're Learning? Assessing Math Concepts.*

Analyzing and Assessing Children's Needs ....

When we assess our children's ability to solve addition and subtraction problems efficiently, it is not enough to know if they can write down answers quickly. Our goals for children's learning go beyond that. We want them to use a variety of strategies to solve problems with flexibility, choosing the method that works best in a particular situation. We want to know if they can use relationships to solve a variety of problems. When we are looking to see what strategies children use, we need to know *how* they got their answers as well as whether the answers are right or wrong. We can determine a good deal about children's understanding of how to solve addition and subtraction problems by observing them at work. The following questions can guide us in our observations.

Questions to Guide Your Observations*

...| **Questions** |...

Addition Problems

- How do the children find the answers to addition problems? Do they count all the objects, or have they developed a more sophisticated strategy? What strategies do they use?

- Do they know the answers to any of the problems without needing to figure them out? If so, what kinds of problems can they solve in this way? For example, do they know "plus-one" problems? doubles? sums to five? sums beyond five?

- Do they figure out problems easily or do they have some difficulty?

- Do they seem to have confidence in their answers?

Subtraction Problems

- How do the children find the answers to subtraction problems? Do they count, or have they developed a more sophisticated strategy? What strategies do they use?

- Do they know the answers to any of the problems without needing to figure them out? If so, what kinds of problems can they solve in this way? For example, do they know "minus-one" problems? differences less than five? differences greater than five?

- Do they figure out problems easily or do they have some difficulty?

- Do they seem to have confidence in their answers?

Size of Numbers

- Do the children solve problems involving numbers to 10 in a way that is different from the way they solve problems involving numbers to 20? If so, how do their methods differ?

* Adapted from *How Do We Know They're Learning? Assessing Math Concepts.*

Meeting the Range of Needs

Because children approach tasks in various ways, those tasks that appear in this chapter will automatically be appropriate for children with differing needs. As they solve the problems presented, the children will either count or they will see relationships. They will solve the problems either with ease or with difficulty.

The questions you ask and the situations you provide can stimulate the children to use more and more sophisticated ways of arriving at answers.

A Classroom Scene ....

While her class is busy with a variety of independent addition and subtraction tasks, Mrs. Buntich is walking around the room observing the children at work. She knows from past experience that most of the children will be working at the level that is challenging for them. While she understands that it is important for the children to develop confidence and ease with addition and subtraction, she also wants to be sure they are thinking about what they are doing and feeling a sense of accomplishment as they work.

Independent Stations: *Solving Addition and Subtraction Problems*

Mrs. Buntich knows that her children represent a range of levels of facility with
number. She expects all her children to be able to read and interpret addition and
subtraction equations at this time. She is interested in seeing how her children
figure out the answers to the problems they are working with. She will especially
watch to see which children are still counting *all* the counters so that she can help
some of them discover more efficient methods for getting answers to addition and
subtraction problems.

Mrs. Buntich stops to watch a group of children who are working with the activity Counting Boards: Think and Write (3–20). When these children worked with the counting boards earlier, they were focused on reading the plus and minus signs and on acting out story problems with the cubes. Now Mrs. Buntich has brought the boards out again to give more practice to the children who need it and to challenge the others to work with the addition and subtraction cards at a higher level.

The children are drawing addition and subtraction cards out of a bag, recording the equations on their worksheets, and then putting the appropriate numbers of cubes on their boards. The teacher has asked them to see if they can figure out the answer to the problem by just looking at the cubes without moving them. She wants to encourage any children who can to try finishing some of the equations without counting each cube. Of course, some of her children still need to count. However, there other children who do know some of the answers to the equations but still count because they think they are supposed to. Mrs. Buntich want to help these children discover that they already know the answers and that they don't need to count.

Lila draws a 4 + 2 card and counts out the number of cubes indicated.

As the girl starts to count all the cubes, Mrs. Buntich asks her, "Do you have an idea of what the total will be?"

Lila stops to think for a moment and says, "I think it will be six."

"Are you sure, or do you need to check?"

"Well, I'm pretty sure."

"If you want to check, that will be fine," Mrs. Buntich tells her. "But I would like you to see if you can think about the problems before you count. Then you can count to check if you need to."

Mrs. Buntich then looks over at Mike. He has chosen the cave counting board and brown cubes. "I'm working with bears," he says, looking up at Mrs. Buntich. She watches him while he does several equations.

Mike draws the 2 + 3 card and writes 2 + 3 = 5 without even using the cubes. Next he draws a 5 − 1 card. "I know that one too," he says, writing 5 − 1 = 4. When he draws 3 + 6, he puts out three cubes and six cubes and counts to see how many. "Oh, nine," he says as he writes the equation.

Mrs. Buntich had asked the children to put out the cubes every time they work with counting boards so that they can work on visualizing the answers to the equations by looking at the cubes. If they find that they already know the answer without needing to count, the children are told to put the card back and to draw another one. Mike, however, is using the task to confirm which combinations he knows and which he doesn't. Mrs. Buntich lets him continue doing the task in the way that works best for him.

Sonja is not able to work at the same level as Mike. Mrs. Buntich is pleased, however, to see that Sonja is able to distinguish between the plus and minus signs with ease. This shows progress, as she used to forget to look carefully at the signs, always adding for both addition and subtraction problems. Sonja is still very methodical when she counts and sometimes loses track of what she is doing. The work with the counting boards is giving her the practice she needs.

Next Mrs. Buntich walks over to the small group doing the activity Build-a-Floor Race (3–15). Pietro and Lex are working with combinations of seven. Lea and Chrissy are working with combinations of five.

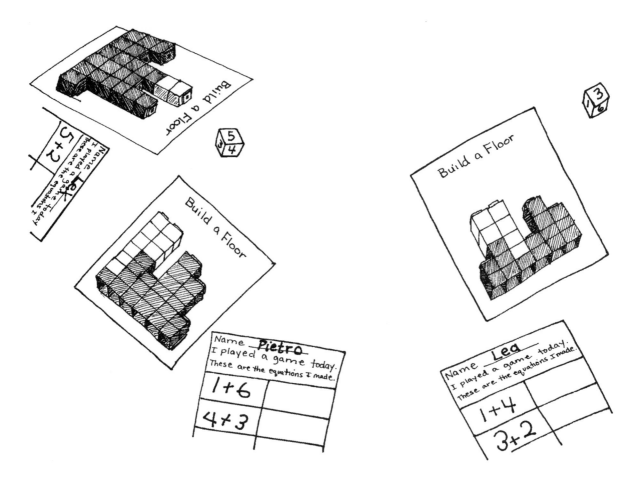

Pietro thinks a bit before he puts his cubes on his game board. He then counts to make sure he has made a train of seven. Lex works somewhat faster but still needs to check to make sure he is right.

When Lea rolls the number cube, she knows immediately whether or not she can use what she rolled.

Maria and Chad are playing Grab-Bag Subtraction (activity 3–22). Chad puts seven cubes into the bag. Maria reaches into the bag and takes out three cubes. She shows them to Chad.

Chad says, "I know there's four left in the bag." He then concentrates while he writes 7 − 3 = 4. Chad is challenged more by writing down the equation than by figuring out the answer.

When it is Maria's turn, she puts six cubes into the bag. Chad reaches in and takes out two. Maria thinks for a minute and says, "I think three are left, or maybe four." She dumps the cubes out of the bag and sees that there are four left. "Oh, yeah. Four." She easily writes 6 − 2 = 4. Mrs. Buntich sees that both children are benefiting from the task and so she moves on.

Anwar and two other children are working with Addition-and-Subtraction Spin It (activity 3–19). Anwar is working confidently and easily with all the number shapes. Mrs. Buntich decides to pose a challenge to him. She presents two shapes and says, "Can you tell me how many these two shapes show together?"

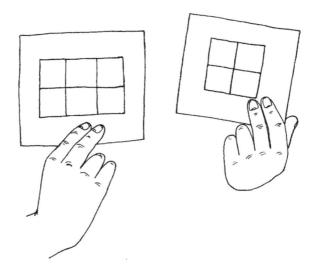

"I think it's ten," he says.

"How did you figure it out?"

"Well, I saw six, and then I counted the others—seven, eight, nine, ten."

Lonnie looks up from his task and joins in. "I think it's ten, too, but I counted by twos, like this." He points to the shapes and indicates how he counted.

The teacher holds up two more number shapes and asks Anwar and the other two children (who are both intrigued and watching by now) to tell how many they think the two shapes show together.

Mrs. Buntich decides that tomorrow she will have a small group stay on the rug and work with her on How Do You See It? Adding Number Shapes (activity 3–29) before they choose stations to work at. She wants to get other children ready to do this task but doesn't want to take them away from their work right now. She appreciates their level of involvement and doesn't want to interrupt it.

$\mathbb{A}$bout the Activities

Developing Strategies for Adding and Subtracting

In this chapter the activities provide opportunities to apply a variety of addition and subtraction strategies. They are to be used for teaching, not for testing. Be aware of this as you are working to help children develop new strategies. Children should always have a way of figuring out an answer. Whichever strategy they need to use to make sense of the problem must be accepted. If children become concerned about using a particular strategy, they often stop trying to make sense of it for themselves and instead try to do what they think the teacher expects.

The children will be learning strategies, not through specific activities designed to develop each one but in the context of their actual problem-solving experiences. It is important that the children see the strategies as useful tools, rather than as ways they've been told to work. The teacher's job is to help identify and label the various strategies as children use them in solving problems.

For practice in applying different strategies, simply present a problem, give the children time to think about it, and then ask them to share their individual ways of determining the answer. The following are strategies that children may use as they move to more and more efficient ways to solve problems:

- Counting on
- Counting back
- Counting up
- Instant recognition of the parts of a number
- Determining the missing parts of a number (relating addition and subtraction)
- Seeing relationships between combinations (doubles plus or minus 1, doubles plus or minus 2)

The independent activities are designed to give children practice adding and subtracting using a variety of strategies. The children should be able to write equations independently before being assigned these tasks.

As always, introduce the independent tasks in a teacher-directed setting. Once introduced, each activity can be done over and over because the tasks are open-ended with the children often creating their own problems.

The first set of activities focuses on developing strategies for numbers to ten. When children are able to work with ease with numbers to ten, they should work with the activities using numbers to 20.

Teacher-Directed Activities

.... | **3–1 Combining Stacks: Pick It Up** | .... **Small-Group Activity**

Materials: Connecting cubes
Preparation: Make five stacks of cubes, each stack a different color and having no more than five cubes.

Show the children your five stacks of cubes. Have them build stacks to match yours. For example:

Build these stacks. Make them exactly like mine.

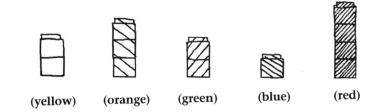

(yellow)   (orange)   (green)   (blue)   (red)

The object of this activity is to find out which numbers it is possible for children to "pick up" using these stacks singly and in combination. The rules are that children may pick up more than one stack at a time, but they may not join stacks together and they may not take any of them apart.

Can you pick up four?

I can. I picked up the red stack.

I found a different way—the yellow stack has two and the green stack has two. That makes four.

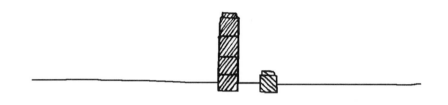

Can you pick up five?

Yes. The red four and the blue one.

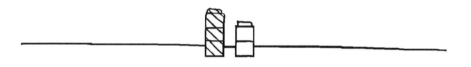

There's another way—the orange three and the yellow two.

I used the orange three but I used the green two.

This activity can be done over and over using different combinations of stacks. Pose such questions as these:

- What happens when you don't have a "one" stack?
- What happens when all the stacks have the same number of cubes?
- What happens when you use all even numbers? all odd numbers?
- What's the largest number we can make with these stacks?
- What's the smallest number we can make?

For a related independent activity, see What Numbers Can You Make? (activity 3–18).

About Instant Recognition of Number Combinations

In Chapter Two, children focused on the combinations that make up a particular number. Children also need to work with combinations of several numbers when they are asked to pay attention to the totals rather than to the parts. In some classrooms this practice is provided through the use of flash cards. Rather than using flash cards with numbers, you can provide more powerful practice by using cards that show arrangements of items that can be counted. When this type of card is used, children have meaningful opportunities to learn what they don't know and to verify what they do know. I refer to such cards as "Meaningful Flash Cards."

Instant recognition of number combinations should be an ongoing part of the math period, allowing children to continually review what they have been learning. Take five or ten minutes on a regular basis to have children practice and review these basic relationships.

Materials: Number Arrangements (See preparation below.)

Preparation: As part of their independent work on internalizing number combinations to 10, the children create "number arrangements" using manipulatives. (See number arrangements activities 2–14 through 2–17.) In the extensions for these activities, children record some of their arrangements on 6" × 9" pieces of paper. Collect a variety of these recordings for use with this small-group work.

As you hold up various number arrangement recordings, have the children say, as fast as they can, how many objects they see. Begin with arrangements of five or less. Hold up one arrangement at a time and ask, "How many?"

When the children can instantly recognize groups of five or less, include groups of more than five. In order to recognize groups of more than five quickly, the children will have to mentally combine the smaller groups that make up the larger ones.

For example, hold up an arrangement.

Tell me fast. How many?

Seven.

How did you know?

'Cause there's four and three, and that's seven.

NOTE: Because it is not always easy for young children to verbalize their mental strategies, showing them how to frame each group with their hands will help them organize what they want to say. Before you ask the children to tell how they know which number is shown by an arrangement, give them a model by saying such things as, "I knew it was seven because I saw four on top and two in the middle and one more." Allowing time for language development is very important. Experiences such as these are valuable aids to clear thinking.

Let's try another one.

How many?

Six.

How did you know?

I saw four on the top and two hanging down. That's six.

Who found a different way?

I saw four in a line down the middle and one on that side and one on that side. That makes six.

How many in this one?

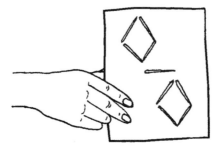

Nine.

How did you know?

'Cause four and four is eight and one more makes nine.

Materials: Number-shape arrangements (See preparation below.)
For the variation: Number shapes for display [BLMs #76–82]
Preparation: As part of their independent work on internalizing number combinations to 10, the children create "number-shape arrangements" using connecting cubes or Color Tiles in two colors and the number shapes. (See activity 2–19.) In the extension, the children record some of their arrangements by coloring them on matching worksheets. Collect a variety of these recordings to use for this small-group work.

As you hold up a number-shape arrangement, have the children describe, as fast as they can, the number combinations they see. For example:

What do you see?

I see two and three makes five.

Who sees it a different way?

I see four reds and one more and that's five.

Here's another one. What do you see?

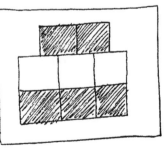

That looks like three and three makes six
and then two more makes eight.

I think three reds and two reds makes five
and three more whites makes eight.

Variation: Hold up blank number shapes. Giving the children opportunities to describe combinations that they can make in the number shapes without color clues frees them to analyze the shapes in their own way. For example:

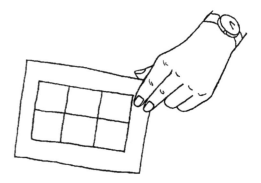

What do you see?

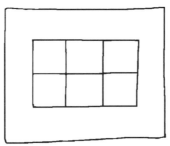

"2" "4" "6"
I see two, four, six.

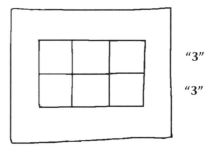

"3"

"3"

I know three and three is six.

"4" "4"
I see four and four makes eight.

How did you see that?

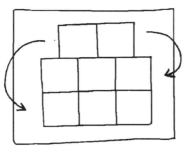

I put one of the top ones with this row and the other top one with the other row, and that makes four and four.

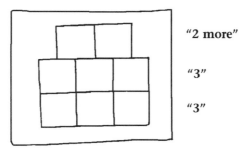

"2 more"

"3"

"3"

I saw three and three makes six and two more makes eight.

"7"   "8"

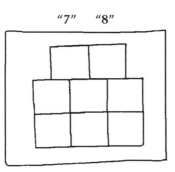

I knew that the bottom was six and I said, "six, seven, eight."

.... Small-Group Activity

Materials: Connecting cubes of two colors joined together in trains of lengths up to 10 (For teacher's use only.)

Hold up a two-color cube train of any length and have the children determine the number of cubes there are of each color and the total number of cubes. For example:

How many blue?

Five.

How did you figure it out?

I saw three blue together and two more. That's five.

Did anyone see it a different way?

I counted and it's five.

How many yellow?

Three.

How many altogether?

Eight.

How did you know?

I knew the blues were five and I counted "five, six, seven, eight."

Who thought of it a different way?

I counted all of them.

Repeat the activity several times using a variety of two-color cube trains.

Materials: Connecting cubes

Provide children with opportunities to discover the relationship between adding doubles and adding doubles plus or minus one. Begin by giving them practice with adding doubles. When this becomes easy for them, show them combinations that are one more or one less than each double respectively. While this gives children the opportunity to see relationships, be aware that not all children will notice these relationships or be able to use them to figure out new problems. Some will see different relationships from the ones you anticipate. Accept whatever they use to figure out the correct answers. For example:

Show one stack.

How many?

    Three.

Show another stack of the same size.

How many altogether?

    Six.

How did you know?

    I saw three and I counted three more.

    'Cause three and three make six.

Sometimes, write the equation on the board.

3 + 3 = 6

Show one stack.

How many?

   Three.

Show another stack with one more.

How many altogether?

   Seven.

How did you know?

   'Cause I counted them.

   Because you had three and three and that was six, but this time you had three and four so that makes seven.

Write the following.

Show one stack.

How many?

   Five.

Show another stack of the same size.

How many altogether?

   Ten.

How did you know it was ten?

   'Cause I just knew that five and five is ten.

Write the following.

Show one stack.

How many?

    Five.

Show a stack with one less.

How many altogether?

    Nine.

How did you know?

    'Cause five and five is ten and that is one less, so it's nine.

    'Cause I knew it was five and I counted four more.

    I knew four and four was eight, but it was five so that makes nine.

Write the following.

Repeat the activity many times so that children can explore a variety of related number combinations.

About the "What Do You Think?" Activities

In this set of activities, children are helped to see that they don't always need to count to find answers. The children are first given counters and are then asked how many counters they *think* they will have if some are added or taken away. Children say what they think—then use counters to check. Children who don't immediately know an answer should get out the appropriate number of counters and use them to figure it out. When the time comes that children know answers without counting, they will no longer need to use the counters.

| 3–6 What Do You Think?
Using Counting Boards | Small-Group Activity |

Materials: Connecting cubes · Counting boards (1 per child) [BLMs #2–6] · Addition cards [BLMs #64–68] and Subtraction cards [BLMs #69–73]

Addition

Select an addition card. As you show the card, tell a number story that fits the counting board setting. Have the children first predict what will happen and then check their prediction. For example:

$4 + 2$

Four ladybugs are crawling in the grass.

The children put four cubes on the "grass" counting board.

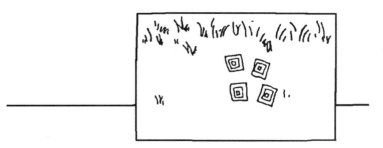

How many ladybugs do you think there will be if two more come?

The children tell how many they think there will be.

Let's check and see.

The children check their predictions with cubes.

Repeat the activity several times using a different addition card each time.

Subtraction

Display a subtraction card and then proceed as you did for addition. For example:

There are six ladybugs crawling in the grass.

How many do you think there will be if three crawl away? How do you know?

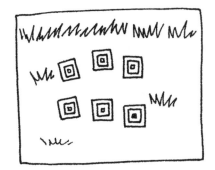

Let's check and see.

Repeat the activity several times using a different subtraction card each time.

3–7 What Do You Think? Using Grab Bags .... Small-Group Activity

Materials: Counters · Paper bag · Addition cards [BLMs #64–68] and Subtraction cards [BLMs #69–73] (optional)

Addition

Display an addition card or write a number combination on the board.

Put counters into the bag to match the first number on the card while the children count with you.

How many are in the bag?

Five.

How many more should we add?

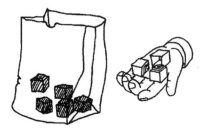

Three.

We put in five, then three more. How many are in the bag now? How do you know?

Repeat the activity several times using a variety of number combinations.

Subtraction

Display a subtraction card or write a subtraction problem on the board.

$$8-4$$

Have the children count with you as you place counters into the bag to match the first number on the card.

We have eight counters in the bag.

Ask a child to take out the second number of counters.

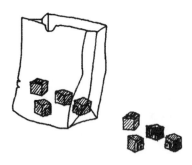

We took away four. How many are left?

Repeat the activity several times, starting with a different number of counters each time.

Materials: Counters · Margarine tub

Addition

Place some counters under a margarine tub and some on top of it and have the children determine the total number. For example:

How many on top?

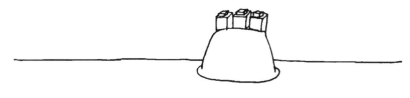

Three.

Lift the tub. How many underneath?

Four.

What is three plus four?

> Six.

> Seven.

> I don't know.

Who can tell me how they figured it out?

> I just remembered that three and four is seven.

> I thought three plus three is six, so three plus four must be seven.

Let's check and see how many.

Three ... four, five, six, seven.

What did we find out?

    Three plus four equals seven.

Repeat the activity several times, using a variety of combinations within the appropriate range of numbers.

Subtraction

Place counters under a margarine tub one by one as the children count them with you. Tip the tub and remove some of the counters. Ask, "How many are under the tub now?" For example:

There are seven counters under the tub.

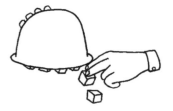

I took out two.

How many are left? How do you know?

Repeat the activity several times, starting with a different number of counters each time.

About the "Let's Pretend" Activities

As you work with some of the standard materials (grab bags, counting boards, number trains, and number shapes), you can help children toward the realization that they can "see the counters in their heads" by asking them to "just pretend" to use counters. Not all children will be ready for this, so treat it lightly. If it seems confusing to some children, avoid asking them to do this for a while. The problem for those who are not ready to visualize the counters is that they may begin to feel that the other children are "magic." Their faith in their own ability to know can be damaged in this way.

The activities described below should help the children feel more confident in their own power to know. Watch the children's reactions. Ask yourself the following. Do the children look puzzled? Are they waiting for others to answer? Are they naming incorrect numbers? The answers to these questions will tell you whether or not the children are ready for these activities.

3–9 Let's Pretend: Grab Bags .... Small-Group Activity

Materials: Paper bag • Counters

In this activity, the counters should be available for checking.

Let's pretend that I put five counters into the bag, and then I put in three more. How many counters will be in the bag? Can you "see" the counters in your head?

Let's put five real counters into the bag now and see if we were right.

Repeat, varying the numbers used.

3–10 Let's Pretend: Counting Boards .... Small-Group Activity

Materials: Counting boards (1 per child) [BLMs #2–6] • Counters

This example is based on the "cave" counting board, although the number story can be adapted for use with any counting board. Have counters available for checking.

Let's pretend three bears are in this cave.

Then two more bears come into the cave. Now how many bears are in the cave?

Can you imagine the bears? Let's try it with counters now and see.

Repeat, varying the numbers used.

Materials: Connecting cubes

The cubes, not needed at first, should be available for checking.

Let's pretend I have a train that is seven cubes long. Suppose I break off three cubes. How many are left?

Now let's use cubes to check and see.

Repeat, varying the numbers.

Let's pretend I have a train of four cubes. I'm adding four more. How long is my train now?

Let's try it with a real cube train and see.

Repeat several times, varying the numbers.

Materials: Number Shapes [BLMs #76–82] · Connecting cubes, wooden cubes, or Color Tiles

In this activity, the cubes or tiles should be available for checking.

Let's pretend we have the "six" number shape and that we filled it partially with four cubes. How many more cubes do we need to fill the whole shape?

Let's pretend that we filled the shape with six cubes. Then let's say we took off two. How many would be left?

Repeat several times, varying the numbers and the shapes.

Independent Activities

Materials: Counters · Counting boards, various settings (2 per child) [BLMs #2–6] · Equations Worksheets [BLM #108]

The child chooses two counting boards and tries to find all the ways that a particular number of counters can be placed on the two boards. The child records each way on a worksheet.

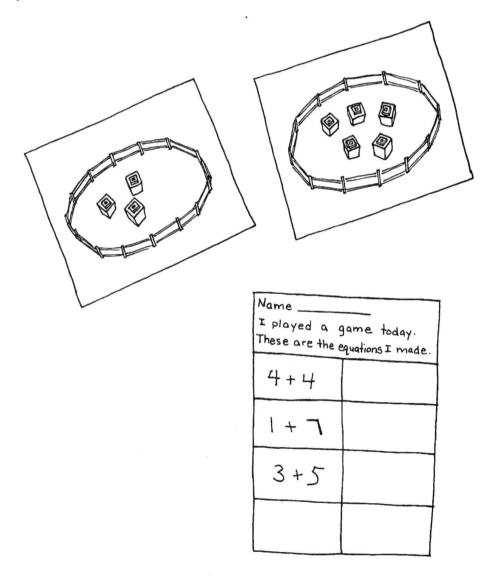

Name _____
I played a game today.
These are the equations I made.

4 + 4	
1 + 7	
3 + 5	

Materials: *Level 1:* Connecting cubes · Game board (See preparation below.) · 0–5 Number cubes (two per child)
Level 2: Same as for Level 1, plus Equations Worksheets (1–2 per child) [BLM #108]
Preparation: Make the game board using one large sheet of paper or two sheets that are taped together so that they can be folded when not in use. Rule the paper into 2-inch squares. Label the top row of squares from 0 to 10.

This game provides a visual display of the number combinations that make up each sum from 1 to 10.

Level 1: Making Combinations

The child rolls the two number cubes, builds two stacks of cubes to match the numbers rolled, and then places the two stacks in a column of the game board according to the *sum* of the numbers rolled. The game is over when one number "wins" (when one column is filled).

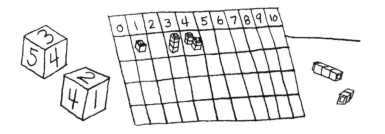

Three and two make five. I'll put these under the five.

Level 2: Writing Equations

Children play the game just as they did in Level 1. When the game is over, they record each number combination on the Equations worksheet. For example:

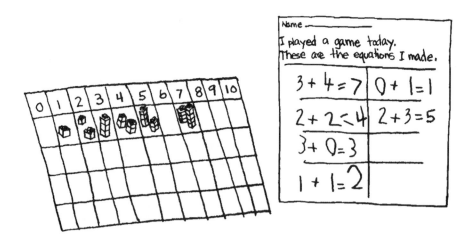

Materials: *Level 1:* Connecting cubes (two colors) ▪ Build-a-Floor Game Boards
(1 per child) [BLM #109] ▪ Number cubes (1 per pair)
Level 2: Same as for Level 1, plus a supply of Equations Worksheets [BLM #108]
Preparation: Duplicate BLM #109 on paper or tagboard. Then cut each copy in half
to make the Build-a-Floor Game Boards.

Level 1: **Making Combinations**

The object of this game is to be the first to complete a "floor" made from
connecting-cube trains lying side by side. Each train must be made from cubes
of two colors (unless zero is rolled). You can assign various sizes for the floors,
depending on the number combinations you want the children to work with.
For example:

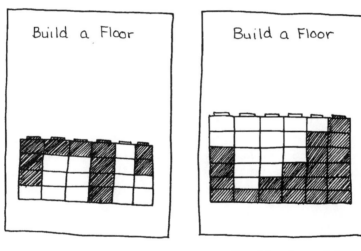

Combinations of 4   Combinations of 6

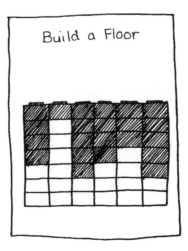

Combinations of 7

In the following example, the children have been told that their completed floor should be five cubes long. In the first stage of the game, the children take turns rolling a number cube to determine the length of the first part (first color) of each train. Each child rolls six times, each time snapping together the indicated number of cubes of that color. Numbers may be repeated.

Player A **Player B**

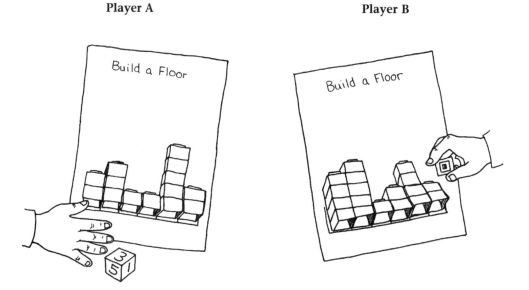

In the second stage of the game, the children take turns rolling the number cube to complete their own floors, placing the indicated number of cubes (of the second color) wherever they can on the board. The second number must combine exactly with one already on the board to finish one train. If children roll a number that they cannot place on their board, they lose that turn.

Player A **Player B**

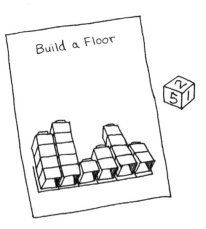

I rolled a four. I can put it with the one of the ones to make five.

I rolled a two. I don't have a three on my board, so I can't play this one.

Play continues until one player completes a floor.

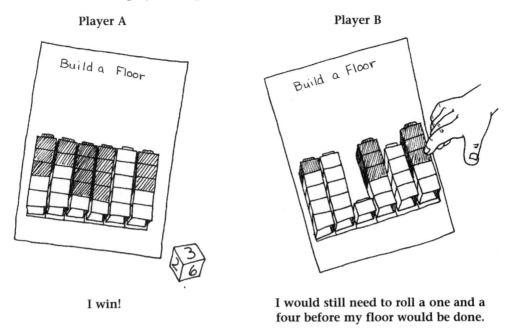

Player A

Build a Floor

I win!

Player B

Build a Floor

I would still need to roll a one and a four before my floor would be done.

NOTE: (Number Cubes) Vary the number cubes to be used according to the number being worked with. For combinations of 4, use cubes numbered 0–4. For combinations of 5, use cubes numbered 0–5. For combinations of 6, use cubes numbered 1–6. For combinations of 7, 8, 9, and 10, use cubes numbered 1–6 and have children add on to complete the floor as needed. For example, assume that a child who is trying to make combinations of 9 rolls a 2. Since there is no 7 on the cube, the child will not be able to complete the train with the second roll. The child will need to add on as many cubes as is indicated by the second roll and then complete the train with a third roll.

Level 2: Writing Equations

The children play the game just as described for Level 1. When they have finished a game, players record their own combinations on an Equations worksheet. (Do not require the use of the worksheet every time the game is played.)

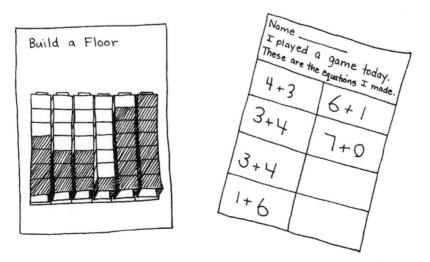

Build a Floor

Name _____
I played a game today.
These are the equations I made.

4 + 3	6 + 1
3 + 4	7 + 0
3 + 4	
1 + 6	

Materials: Connecting cubes · Apartment Buildings Game Boards (1 per child)
[BLM #112, cut in half] · 0–4 Number cubes (1 per pair or group)

This game offers effective practice with the relationships involved in adding and
subtracting.

The children build "apartment buildings" (stacks of connecting cubes) on each
"lot" (box) on their game boards. Each completed apartment building must have
the same number of stories. (The teacher assigns a number or the children choose
and agree on a number.) Each building "under construction" must be completed
before a new building can be started.

The children roll a number cube to determine the number of stories they can add
to their buildings. The child who completes all of his or her apartment buildings
first is the winner. For example:

For this game, the children have decided that each building is to be four stories high.

Player A

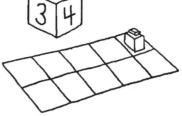

I rolled a three. My first building
has three stories so far.

Player B

I rolled a one. I can build one
story of my first building.

Player A

I rolled a two. I need one of the two
cubes for my first building. I can start
a new building with the other cube.

Player B

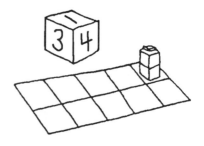

I rolled a one again. I can put another
story on my building. I need two
more cubes to finish my building.

Player A

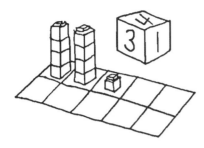

Player B

I rolled a four. I can put three stories on my second building and I have one more to start my next building.

I rolled a three. I can put two on my first building. I have one more to start my next one.

The players continue taking turns rolling the number cube and building apartment buildings until one player has filled all ten lots with four-story buildings.

NOTE: This game is very effective, but somewhat complicated. Most children will need to have the game modeled several times before they are able to play it independently. It can be introduced to a small group as a teacher-directed activity, with each child in the group constructing buildings on his or her own game board. Then, rather than competing to be the first to complete the buildings, the children simply practice building them, with everyone adding cubes to their buildings simultaneously according to each roll of the number cube. For example:

Tell the group that each apartment building is to be six cubes high. Guide children through the building steps as follows.

Shanika rolled a three. Everyone, make your first apartment building three stories high.

Andre rolled a four. Everyone, get four cubes. How many of the cubes do you need to finish your first building? How many will you have left to start your next one?

Materials: Connecting cubes or wooden cubes · Shape Puzzles [BLMs #34–36] ·
2" × 6" strips of paper
For the extension: Shape Puzzles [BLMs #37–40]

The child selects several puzzles, fills each one with cubes, and then writes an addition equation for each puzzle to describe how the "parts" can be combined to make the whole. Most puzzles can be described with more than one equation. Each equation should be written on a separate strip of paper.

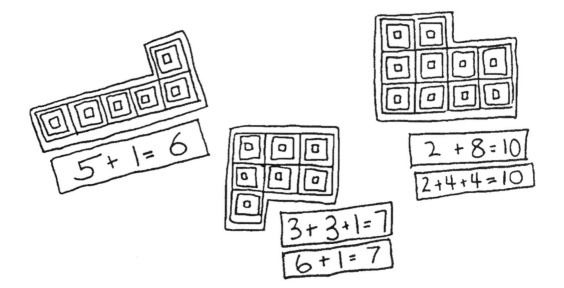

The equations for each puzzle can be stapled together to form a small book.

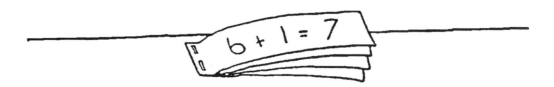

Extension: When the children are ready to work with combinations to 20, provide them with the larger shape puzzles, BLMs #37–40, and have them write equations to describe these puzzles.

Materials: Connecting cubes · Crayons · Making Numbers Worksheets (1 two-page set per child) [BLMs #110–111]
For the variation: Provide Counting Worksheets [BLM #33] in place of the Making Numbers Worksheets.

Before trying this independent activity, most children will benefit from working with the teacher-directed activity Combining Stacks: Pick It Up (3–1).

The child starts by making five one-color trains, each of a different color and having up to five cubes. More than one train may have any particular number of cubes.

The object is to try to use the five trains in combination to make each of the numbers from one to ten in as many ways as possible. Any number of trains can be combined to make a number, but the original trains may not be broken apart.

Every time a child makes a number, he or she colors a corresponding outline on the worksheet to show the trains of each color and then writes the equation that describes the trains used.

Carefully model the use of the worksheet. Start by displaying the five trains. For example:

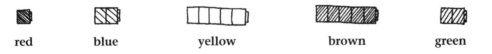

red   blue   yellow   brown   green

Name _____

| 1 | 2 | 5 | 5 | 2 |

3   1 + 2 = 3
    1 + 2 = 3

4   2 + 2 = 4

5   2 + 2 + 1 = 5

6

7

* Based on *Mathematics Their Way,* "Addition with Unifix Cubes," p. 246.

The activity can be done over and over, as each group of trains of different lengths will provide a new experience.

Challenge the children with questions like these:

- What happens when you don't have a "one" train?
- What happens when all the trains show the same number?
- What happens when you use all even-number trains? all odd-number trains?
- What's the largest number we can make with all these trains?
- What's the smallest number we can make?

Variation: Have the children repeat the activity using their five-cube trains to make each of the numbers from one to ten in as many ways as possible. However, this time, have them record their results by making a graph on the Counting Worksheet. If they can't make a particular number, they cross it out. If they can make the number, they record each combination they use to make it. Note that some combinations will be repeated if children have different-colored trains of the same length.

Carefully model the use of the worksheet. For example:

| red | blue | green | orange | black |

I made four lots of ways: two red and two blue, two
blue and two black, and two red and two black.
I think I can make seven lots of ways, too.

Materials: Connecting cubes or Color Tiles (in two colors) • Number Shapes [BLMs #76–82] • Plus-or-Minus Spinner (1 per child) • Equations Worksheets (1 per child) [BLM #108]
For the variation: Number-Train Outlines [BLMs #91–98]

Have available a variety of number shapes with which the children have already worked. A child chooses one of the number shapes and spins the spinner to determine whether to add or subtract. If the spinner lands on *plus,* the child uses any combination of cubes of two colors to fill the number shape and then records what was done on the worksheet. If the spinner lands on *minus,* the child uses cubes of one color to fill the number shape and then removes some of the cubes and writes an equation to record this. The child then selects another number shape and repeats the activity. For example:

The child picks this number shape.

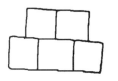

The child spins the spinner. It lands on *plus.*

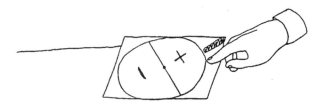

The child puts cubes of two colors on the number shape and writes the equation.

The child chooses another shape and spins the spinner again. This time, the spinner lands on *minus*.

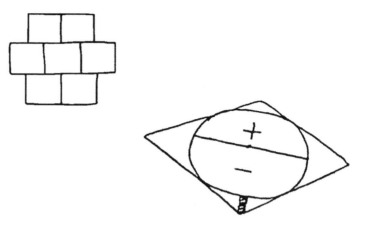

The child fills the number shape with cubes of one color and then takes some cubes off and writes the equation.

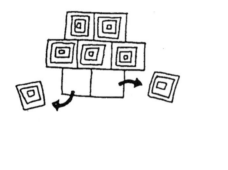

Variation: Have children repeat the activity using Number-Train Outlines in place of the number shapes.

Materials: Counters · Counting boards, any setting (1 per child) [BLMs #2–6] ·
Addition Cards [BLMs #64–68] and Subtraction Cards [BLMs #69–73] · Paper bag ·
Equations Worksheets [BLM #108]

Place the addition and subtraction cards into the paper
bag. Have a child draw a card from the bag and place the
appropriate number of counters on a counting board
according to the following.

If the child draws an addition card, he or she first places
the counters to match the first number on the card. Then, before placing the counters to match the second number, the child tries to think of the total. A child who
is sure of the total may write it on a worksheet. A child who is not sure should
place the second number of counters on the board and then determine the total.

If the child draws a subtraction card, he
or she places counters to match the first
number on the card. Then, before remov-
ing counters as indicated by the second
number, the child tries to think about
how many would be left if that many
counters were removed. A child who is
not sure should remove the second number of counters from the board and then
count to check how many are left.

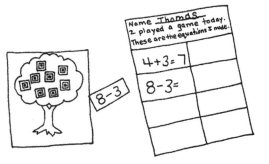

NOTE: This task is designed to help the children think about adding and subtracting mentally while they still have physical models to help them. Be sure that the
children put out the first number of counters each time so that they won't try to
simply count on their fingers instead of visualizing what would happen with the
counters. If some children resist putting out any counters because they already
know the answer to the problem on the card they drew, tell them to put that card
back into the bag and to keep drawing until they draw a problem that they still
have to think about.

3–21 Grab-Bag Addition Station

.... Independent Activity for Partners

Materials: Counters · Paper bag · Small chalkboard, chalk, and eraser for each child

One partner puts some counters into a paper bag, naming the number selected. The other partner does the same.

I put in six.   I put in two.

Both partners write the number combination on their chalkboards and predict how many counters are in the bag altogether.

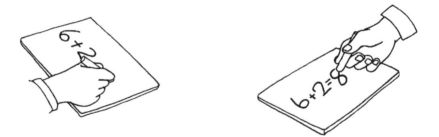

The children then pour the counters out of the bag and count them to check the total.

Limit the number of counters the children use by having them choose from a collection of a given number.

Materials: Counters · Paper bag · Small chalkboard, chalk, and eraser or Equations Worksheet for each child [BLM #108]

One partner fills the bag with some number of counters. The other partner reaches into the bag, takes out some counters, and shows what he or she has taken. Partners each predict how many counters they think are left in the bag. Then they check their predictions, and each child records the subtraction equation on a chalkboard or on a worksheet.

We had five cubes in the bag.

I think there are three left.

So do I.

Let's check and see.

For a description of Grab-Bag Subtraction as a teacher-directed activity, see activity 2–6.

Materials: Connecting cubes (two colors) · Small chalkboard, chalk, and eraser for each child

One partner makes and holds up a two-color cube train. The other partner writes the corresponding addition equation on a chalkboard.

Partners take turns being the one to make the two-color train (with up to ten cubes) and being the one to record the addition equation for the train.

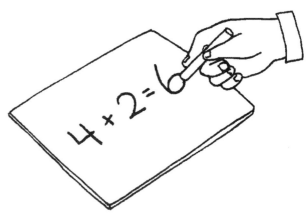

.... **Independent Activity for Partners**

Materials: Counters • Margarine tub (1 per pair) • Small chalkboard, chalk, and eraser for each child

The first partner chooses some counters, displays them, and then puts them under the tub. Then that partner puts additional counters on top of the tub. The second partner writes the addition equation represented. If the second partner does not know the total, then the first partner lifts the tub. Together they check the total. For example:

I put three counters under the tub.

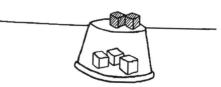

I put two counters on top of the tub.

How many counters are there altogether?

The partners lift the tub to check.

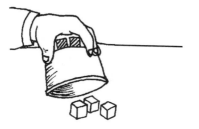

Yes, two plus three is five.

Partners take turns being the one to place the counters (up to a total of ten) and being the one to write the addition equation.

Materials: Connecting cubes • Small chalkboard, chalk, and eraser for each child

The first partner makes a cube train, shows it to the other partner, and then with the train hidden behind his or her back, breaks off some cubes and asks how many are left.

I made a train that is six cubes long.

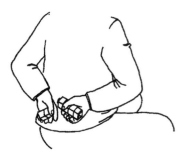

I broke off four.

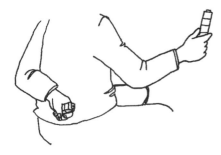

How many cubes are left behind my back?

The second partner writes the equation.

The first partner shows what was hidden so that they can check the answer together.

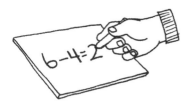

Yes, I had two left behind my back.

Partners repeat the activity, taking turns making up problems. They use a variety of numbers with a total of ten or less.

Materials: Counters (one color) • Number Shapes [BLMs #76–82] • Small chalkboard, chalk, and eraser for each child

One partner starts a subtraction problem by using counters to fill a number shape.

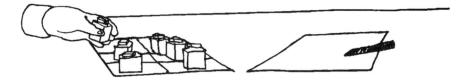

The second partner closes his or her eyes while the first partner removes some of the counters.

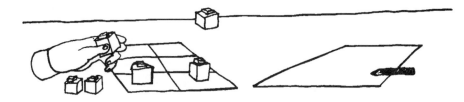

The second partner then looks at what is remaining and writes the equation to tell what happened.

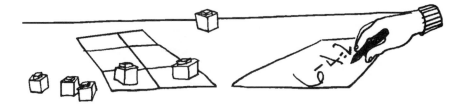

The partners then switch roles and begin the activity again.

Materials: Connecting cubes (two colors) • Addition Cards [BLMs #64–68] • More-or-Less Spinners (1 per pair) (See Materials Preparation for Plus-or-Minus Spinner, p. 15.)
For the variation: As for above, plus Subtraction Cards [BLMs #69–73]

Players put the addition cards facedown in a pile. Each player draws one card.

Using cubes of two colors, both players build a train to match their cards.

One player spins the spinner. If it lands on *less*, the player with less cubes wins both stacks. If the spinner lands on *more*, the player with more cubes wins both stacks.

It landed on *less*. I win!

Players continue in the same way, each accumulating trains according to their spin.

When time is up or when the children decide to end the game, they each snap together all the trains they have won into one long train. They compare their long trains. Then they spin the spinner one last time to see if the player who has accumulated *more* cubes or the one who has accumulated *less* is the overall winner.

Variation: Have the children repeat the game, this time using both the addition and the subtraction cards.

Teacher-Directed Activities

About Number Combinations to 20

The work that children do with numbers to 20 depends in large part on their understanding of the relationships between pairs of numbers to ten. The following activities help children develop a way to think about numbers to 20 using similar relationships.

If your checks for readiness indicate any hesitation on the part of the children, give them more time to become comfortable with numbers to ten before introducing these activities.

3–28 Related Combinations: Tall Stacks .... **Whole-Class or Small-Group Activity**

Materials: Connecting cubes

This activity is just like Related Combinations: Short Stacks (3–5) except that in this activity the children are working with larger numbers. Begin by giving children practice with "doubles." When they find doubles easy, show them combinations that are one more or one less than the doubles. While this gives children the opportunity to see relationships, be aware that not all children will notice these relationships or be able to use them to figure out new problems. Accept whichever ways they use to figure out a correct answer. For example:

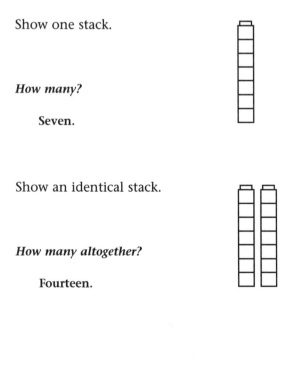

Show one stack.

How many?

    Seven.

Show an identical stack.

How many altogether?

    Fourteen.

How did you know?

    I saw seven and counted seven more.

    I know seven and seven makes fourteen.

    I counted "seven, eight, nine, ten" and then I saw four more and that makes fourteen.

Sometimes, write the equation on the board.

Show one stack.

How many?

    Seven.

Show another stack with one more.

How many altogether?

    Fifteen.

How did you know?

    'Cause I counted them.

    Because you had seven and seven and that was fourteen, but this time you had seven and eight, so that makes fifteen.

Write the following.

Show one stack.

How many?

Nine.

Show another identical stack.

How many altogether?

Eighteen.

How did you know it was eighteen?

'Cause I thought 10 and 10 was 20, but I had to take off one of those and one of those, so that makes 18.

Write the following.

Show one stack.

How many?

Nine.

Show a stack with one less.

How many altogether?

Seventeen.

How did you know?

> I saw the nine and I knew I needed one more to make a ten. So that would leave seven so that has to be seventeen.

> 'Cause I saw nine and I counted the other stack and I got to seventeen.

> I knew eight and eight. That's sixteen. But this was eight and nine.

Write 9 + 8 = 17.

Repeat the activity several times so that children can explore a variety of related number combinations.

Materials: *Level 1:* Several of each of the Number Shapes [BLMs #76–82]
Level 2: Same as for Level 1, plus small chalkboard, chalk, and eraser for each child

Be sure that the children are ready for this activity, in which they add numbers using the number shapes. To do this, the children must know the numbers needed to fill each shape without counting. You can check their readiness by holding up each of the number shapes. Say, "Thumbs up as soon as you know how many squares are in the shape." If the children respond quickly, go ahead with this activity. If they do not, give them practice in identifying the shapes until they know the numbers without counting.

Level 1: **Developing Addition Strategies**

Hold up two number shapes and ask the children to state the problem by naming the two shapes. For example:

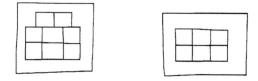

Eight and six.

Put your thumb up as soon as you think you know the total.

After allowing some time for the children to determine the total, ask:

How did you see it?

Give several children a chance to explain their strategies. As each child explains, write the related equation on the chalkboard. For example:

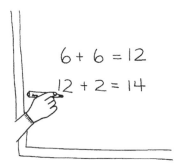

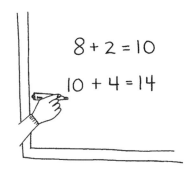

I saw six and six is twelve and two more makes fourteen.

I saw eight and two more makes ten. Then there's four more and that's fourteen.

Let's try a different pair of number shapes.

Five and six.

I saw six and then I counted "seven, eight, nine, ten, eleven."

I saw if it was six and six it would be twelve, but one is off, so it's eleven.

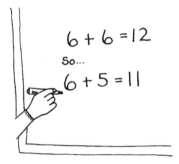

Repeat the activity several times using various combinations of number shapes.

Variation: You can add a little fun to the task by making two facedown stacks of number shapes, turning the top two cards over quickly and then challenging the children to try and figure out the totals as quickly as possible.

Level 2: **Writing Equations**

Conduct the activity as for Level 1, but now have the children use their individual chalkboards to write the equations they see.

For a related independent activity, see Number-Shape Pairs (activity 3–33).

Materials: Counters (two colors) • Number Shapes (10), (2 per child) [BLM #82] or Clear-the-Deck Game Boards (1 per child) [BLM #74] • 4–9 Number cubes

Addition: Ten Plus a Number Have the children fill one of their ten-shapes with ten counters of one color. They take turns rolling the number cube and adding counters of a different color to their second ten-shape according to the number rolled. Then they determine how many counters they have altogether.

Record the problem on the chalkboard.

Repeat the activity several times. Once the children understand the ten-plus pattern and know the totals without counting, go on to Nine Plus a Number.

Addition: Nine Plus a Number The children fill one of their ten-shapes with nine counters of one color. As before, they take turns rolling the number cube to determine how many counters to add. Using counters of a second color, they add one counter to complete the first shape and place the remaining counters on the other shape. Then they determine how many counters there are altogether.

Record the problem on the chalkboard.

Repeat the activity several times. Once the children understand the nine-plus pattern and know the totals without counting, go on to Eight Plus a Number.

Addition: Eight Plus a Number The children fill in the first ten-shape with eight counters of one color and then roll the number cube to determine how many counters to add. They use the second color to complete the first shape with two of the counters and place the remaining counters on the other shape.

Write the problem.

Repeat the activity several times.

Mixing Them Up Repeat the activity several times, randomly starting each time with either eight, nine, or ten counters.

Subtraction: Minus Ten Write a number between 10 and 20 on the chalkboard. Tell the children to use counters to show that number on their two ten-shapes.

Say "Minus ten," and have the children put their thumbs up when they know the answer. Have them tell how they figured it out.

Repeat the activity several times.

When the children see the minus-ten pattern and know the remainders without counting, go on to Minus Nine.

Subtraction: Minus Nine Write a number between nine and twenty on the chalkboard, and have the children build that number on their two ten-shapes.

Say "Minus nine," and have the children put their thumbs up when they think they know the answer. Have them tell how they figured it out.

Repeat the activity several times, each time starting with a different number.

Materials: Several of each of the Number Shapes [BLMs #76–82] (For teacher use only.)

Be sure that the children are ready for this activity, which requires that they instantly know the total of ten plus any single-digit number (such as 10 + 5 and 10 + 8) as well as the difference of ten (for problems such as 16 − 6 and 15 − 5). You can check children's readiness by showing the ten-shape and one other number shape. Then have children indicate the total. For example, show these shapes:

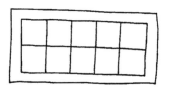 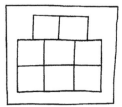

Tell me fast. How many altogether?

Eighteen.

Repeat with other pairs of shapes until you are sure that children know the combinations with ten.

Then show the ten-shape and one other number shape.

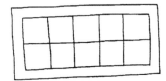 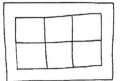

How many?

Sixteen.

Take away six. How many now?

Ten.

If the children consistently know the answers to both types of problems, then they are ready for the following subtraction activity.

To help develop subtraction strategies, show the ten-shape and one other number shape, asking the children to indicate the total. Direct them to take away several different numbers from this total, each time having them tell how many remain. Have them explain how they figured it out. For example:

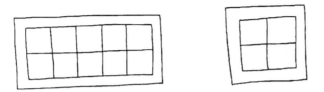

That's fourteen.

Take away three. How many now?

Eleven.

How did you know?

If you take three from four, you have one. One and ten make eleven.

Repeat the activity several times using a variety of number shapes along with the ten-shape.

3–32 Exploring Number Relationships with the Magic Box*

.... **Small-Group Activity**

Materials: Magic Box and Magic Box Cards (See preparation below.) · Number lines made from Pattern-Train Outlines [BLM #60] · Connecting cubes
Preparation: Prepare a magic box and magic box cards as described below.
To make the number lines, make a copy of the Pattern-Train Outlines and label each strip on the copy with the numerals from 0 to 13. Duplicate this copy to provide one number line for each child. Cut apart the three lines and mount each on a strip of tagboard.

Making the Magic Box

The magic box is designed so that when a magic box card is placed into the top slot, it turns inside the box so that the number on the back appears when the card comes out of the bottom slot—like magic!

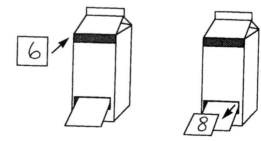

* Based on *Mathematics Their Way,* "The Magic Box," p. 248.

Magic Box

Cut a half-inch slit across the top of a half-gallon milk carton. Cut another half-inch slit across the bottom.

Slip a 3" × 12" piece of tagboard through the top slot and push it out through the bottom slot. This will be easier to manage if you open up the milk carton so that you can get your hand inside it. Tape the strip at the top to hold it in place. When this is done, staple the carton closed again.

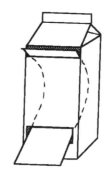

Pull out an inch or so of the strip at the bottom and tape the back of it to the carton. When you place a card in through the top slot of the magic box, holding it so that you are looking at the number on the front, the card will turn over inside the carton so that when it comes out of the bottom slot the number on the back appears. To test your magic box, place a card in through the top slot to see if it slides down the strip easily.

Magic Box Cards

The magic box is used with sets of cards, each reflecting a particular number relationship. The number that appears on the front of each card is related to the number that appears on the back. That is, the number on the front of each card in a set is a certain amount more or less than the number on the back.

Make sets of cards that have the number relationships you want your children to experience. Each set should include eight to twelve cards. Make each set a different color so that you can easily sort the cards. For example, you might write the numbers on the front of the plus-one cards in green, the minus-two cards in blue, and so forth. Write the numbers on the backs of the cards in black. The children will then learn to put the cards into the box colored-side up to see which black number will come out. The following are examples of card sets.

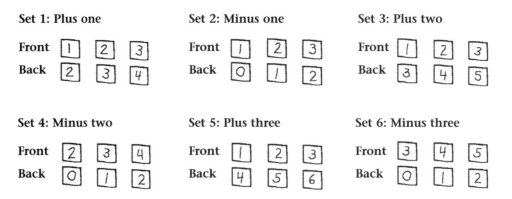

Using the Magic Box

The children discover number relationships and make predictions based on these relationships.

Give a number line to each child. Have one child choose a magic box card from the set you have provided and then hold it up so that the rest of the group can see it. Have all the children place that number of cubes on their number lines.

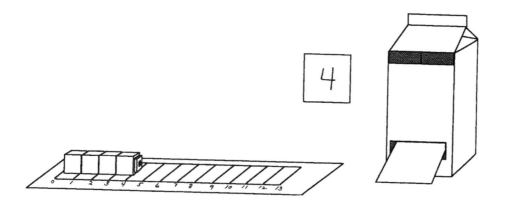

The child who chose the card places it into the top slot of the magic box and then shows the group the black numeral that appears on the back of the card when it comes out of the bottom slot. The children then add cubes to or subtract cubes from their number lines until they reach the number indicated on the back of the card.

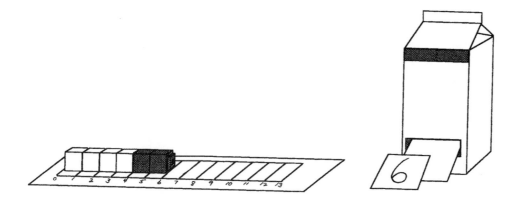

We put two more cubes on to make six. Six is two more than four.

Another child chooses a magic box card and shows the colored numeral to the rest of the group. The children show that number of cubes on their number lines.

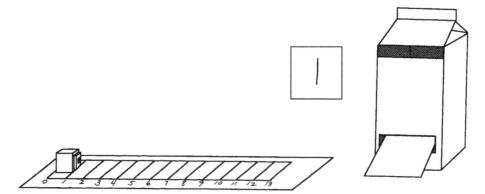

After the card is placed into the slot and the black numeral appears, the children add and subtract cubes until they reach the number indicated on the card.

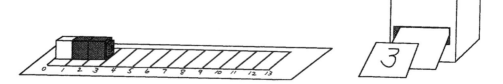

Have children do three examples with a given set of cards. Then, after the next child picks a card and shows it to the group, ask the group to predict what number they think will come out of the magic box. In the above examples, the number on the back of the card is two more than the number on the front, which many children will be able to predict. Be sure that children put the cards through the magic box to check their predictions.

On successive days, repeat the activity using a different set of cards so that the children will have new patterns to discover.

Variation: Mix up the cards so that there is no particular pattern for the children to discover. Have children instead figure out the relationships between a variety of numbers. For example:

We start with seven.

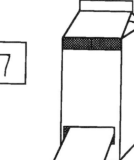

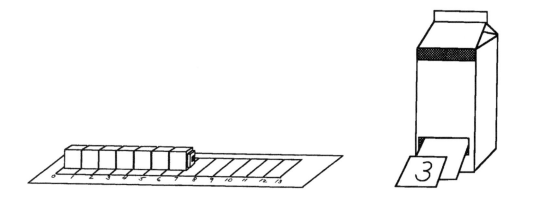

What do we have to do to get to three? Do we add or subtract?

Write the problem on the board.

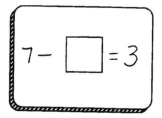

Read the problem aloud as "Seven take away what number makes three?"

We had to break four off to get to the three.

Write the number in the equation.

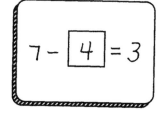

Another child chooses a card and shows it to the others.

This time we start with ten.

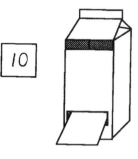

All the children then place ten cubes on their number lines.

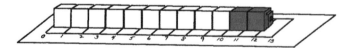

The card is placed into the slot and the children find out what number appears this time.

We got a twelve.

Do we need to add or subtract to get to twelve?

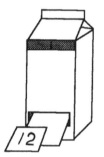

Write the equation as you ask, "Ten plus what number equals twelve?"

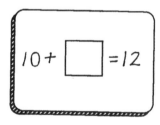

$10 + \boxed{} = 12$

We need to add two more.

Write the numeral in the equation as the children report the number they added.

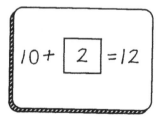

$10 + \boxed{2} = 12$

Independent Activities

Materials: Connecting cubes or Color Tiles (optional) · Number Shapes (several of each) [BLMs #76–82] · Paper and pencil

The child picks two number shapes and writes the equation represented by that combination. Children may choose to fill the shapes with counters, but doing so is not required. Encourage children to figure out the sums without counting each square.

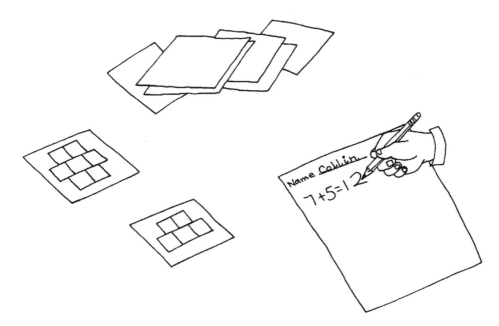

For a related teacher-directed activity, see How Do You See It? Adding Number Shapes (activity 3–29).

Materials: Counters (in two colors) · 4–9 Number cubes (1 per child) · Number Shapes (10), two per child [BLM #82] · Numeral Cards 11–20 (for subtraction) [BLMs #18–19] · Equations Worksheets [BLM #108]

Addition

The children each use two ten-shapes. They roll the number cube twice to determine how many counters to place on each ten-shape. Then they place the counters on the ten-shapes and find the total.

Encourage children to use the shapes to help them add.

NOTE: For this activity, there is no specified way of placing the counters. The children should be allowed to use the ten-shapes in any way that makes it easier for them to add.

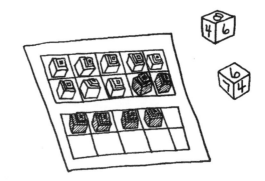

I need two of the six to make a ten. Ten and four make fourteen.

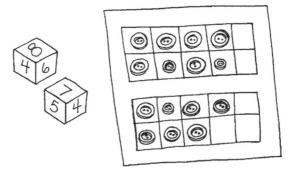

I think it is fifteen because eight and eight is sixteen,
but there is one less on this one.

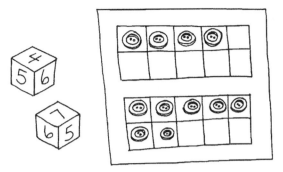

**I need three more to make ten. There would be
one left, so that would make it eleven.**

Subtraction

The children make up problems, each child using two ten-shapes. Then they record
the problems on a worksheet.

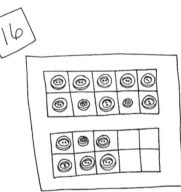

Mix up the numeral cards. The child
draws a card and builds the number
shown by putting counters on the
ten-shapes.

The child then rolls the number cube, takes that many counters off the ten-
shape(s), and records the appropriate equation on the Equations Worksheet.

Materials: Connecting cubes or Color Tiles (optional) • Number Shapes (several of each) [BLMs #76–82] • Number cubes • Equations Worksheets [BLM #108]

Each child takes a ten-shape and one other shape and writes the total. (Some children will choose to fill the number shapes with counters, while others will simply consider the number of squares that make up each number shape.)

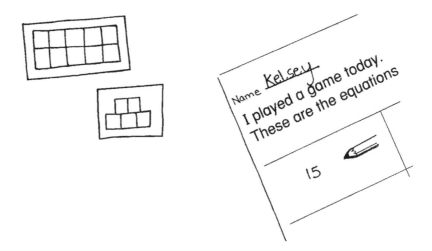

The child then rolls a number cube to determine how many to take away and records the equation on a worksheet. For example:

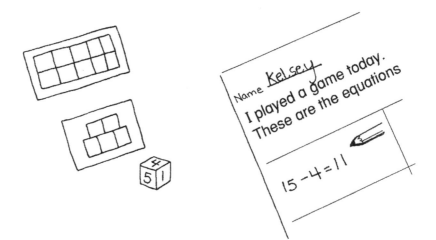

Have children repeat the activity, each time taking a ten-shape along with a different number shape.

Materials: Connecting cubes · 0–5, 1–6, and 4–9 Number Cubes (1 per child) · Paper and pencil · 00–99 chart (1 per child) [BLM #116]

The child chooses a number cube, rolls once, doubles the number rolled, and then uses cubes to build two stacks to show the double. The child writes the equation and also circles the sum on the 00–99 chart. Have the children explore these questions:

■ What numbers do you get when you double the rolls of each number cube?

■ Are there any numbers you don't get? Which ones?

■ Are there any other numbers you want to try that aren't on your number cubes?

Four and four.   Three and three.   Five and five.

00	01	02	03	04	05	06	07	08	09
10	11	12	13	14	15	16	17	18	19
20	21	22	23	24	25	26	27	28	29
30	30	32	33	34	35	36	37	38	39
40	41	42	23	44	45	46	47	48	49
50	51	52	53	54	55	56	57	58	59
60	61	62	63	64	65	66	67	68	69
70	71	72	73	74	75	76	77	78	79
80	81	82	83	84	85	86	87	88	89
90	91	92	93	94	95	96	97	98	99

Beth

$4 + 4 = 8$
$3 + 3 = 6$
$5 + 5 = 10$

The children should begin with small numbers, using the 0–5 or 1–6 number cube. After they are confident at this level, allow them to use the 4–9 number cube.

Variation: The children can practice the "doubles-plus-one" combinations in the same way, rolling the number cube and thinking "double plus one." They record the resulting equation.

Miles

$1 + 2 = 3$
$2 + 3 = 5$

Materials: Counters · Clear-the-Deck Gameboard (1 per child) [BLM #74] · Plus-or-Minus Spinner · Paper and pencil

The children begin by each filling their game board with 20 counters and writing "20" on their paper. They take turns spinning the spinner and rolling the number cube to see whether to add counters or to take counters off their game boards. At the end of each turn, children record the number of counters on their boards.

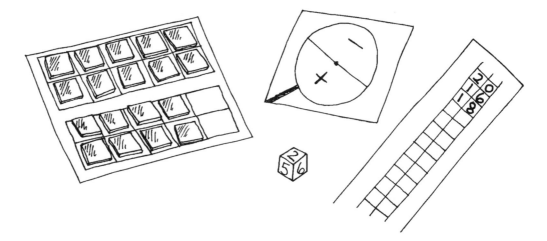

If, on a turn, the number of counters rolled won't fit, the child loses that turn.

Whoever is first to clear his or her game board is the winner.

Here is a complete list of the blackline masters included in the *Developing Number Concepts* series. The masters that are to be used with *Book Two* are listed in heavy type.

1 **Working-Space Paper**
2 **Counting Boards (Tree/Ocean)**
3 **Counting Boards (Barn/Cave)**
4 **Counting Boards (Corral/Store)**
5 **Counting Boards (Road/House)**
6 **Counting Boards (Garden/Grass)**
7 Creation Cards (Doorway/Pig)
8 Creation Cards (Tree/Caterpillar)
9 Creation Cards (Horse/Giraffe)
10 Creation Cards (Dog/Table)
11 Creation Cards (Slide/Fireplace)
12 Creation Cards (Robot/Bench)
13 Small Dot Cards (1–10 dots)
14 Numeral Cards 0–6 (front)
15 Numeral Cards 0–6 (back)
16 Numeral Cards 0–10 (front)
17 Numeral Cards 0–10 (back)
18 **Numeral Cards 11–20 (front)**
19 **Numeral Cards 11–20 (back)**
20 Tell-Me-Fast Dot Cards
21 Tell-Me-Fast Dot Cards
22 Tell-Me-Fast Dot Cards
23 Tell-Me-Fast Dot Cards
24 Tell-Me-Fast Dot Cards
25 Tell-Me-Fast Dot Cards
26 Tell-Me-Fast Dot Cards
27 Tell-Me-Fast Dot Cards
28 **Number Lines (1–10)**
29 **Number Lines (1–20)**
30 Roll-a-Tower Game Board (1–6)
31 Roll-a-Tower Game Board (4–9)
32 Build a City/Building Stacks
   Game Board
33 **Counting Worksheet**
34 **Shape Puzzles (3–6)**
35 **Shape Puzzles (7–10)**
36 **Shape Puzzles (7–10)**
37 **Shape Puzzles (10–20)**
38 **Shape Puzzles (10–20)**
39 **Shape Puzzles (10–20)**
40 **Shape Puzzles (10–20)**
41 Line Puzzles (3–6)
42 Line Puzzles (3–6)
43 Line Puzzles (3–6)

44 Line Puzzles (3–6)
45 Line Puzzles (7–10)
46 Line Puzzles (7–10)
47 Line Puzzles (7–10)
48 Line Puzzles (10–20)
49 Line Puzzles (10–20)
50 Line Puzzles (10–20)
51 Line Puzzles (10–20)
52 Line Puzzles (10–20)
53 Line Puzzles (10–20)
54 Line Puzzles (10–20)
55 Line Puzzles (10–20)
56 Hands Worksheet
57 Measure-It Worksheet
58 Fill-It Worksheet
59 Colors Worksheet
60 **Pattern-Train Outlines**
61 Rhythmic-Motions Pictures
62 More/Less/Same Cards
63 More/Less/Same Worksheet
64 **Addition Cards (Sums to 6)**
65 **Addition Cards (Sums to 6)**
66 **Addition Cards (Sums of 7 to 9)**
67 **Addition Cards (Sums of 7 to 9)**
68 **Addition Cards (Sums of 10)**
69 **Subtraction Cards (Subtracting
   from 1 to 6)**
70 **Subtraction Cards (Subtracting
   from 1 to 6)**
71 **Subtraction Cards (Subtracting
   from 7 to 9)**
72 **Subtraction Cards (Subtracting
   from 7 to 9)**
73 **Subtraction Cards (Subtracting
   from 10)**
74 **Clear-the-Deck Game Board**
75 **Hiding Assessment Recording
   Sheet**
76 **Number Shapes (4)**
77 **Number Shapes (5)**
78 **Number Shapes (6)**
79 **Number Shapes (7)**
80 **Number Shapes (8)**
81 **Number Shapes (9)**
82 **Number Shapes (10)**

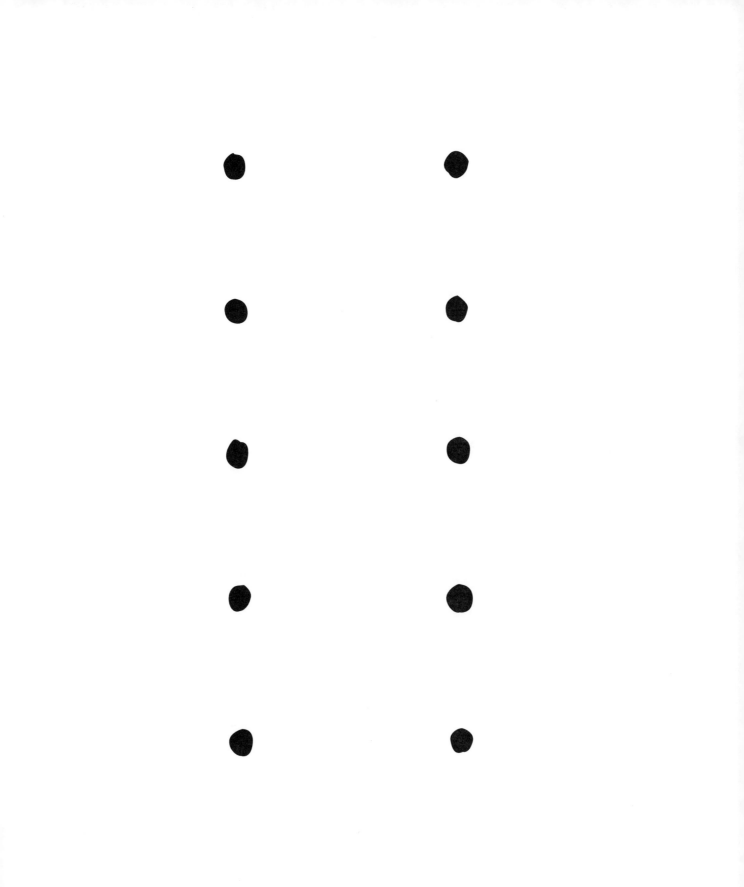

Tree

— · — · — · — · — · — · — · — · — · — · — cut — · — · — · — · — · — · — · — · — · — · —

Ocean

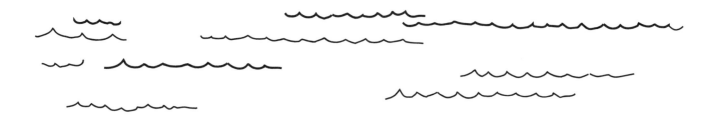

   Counting Boards

Barn

Cave

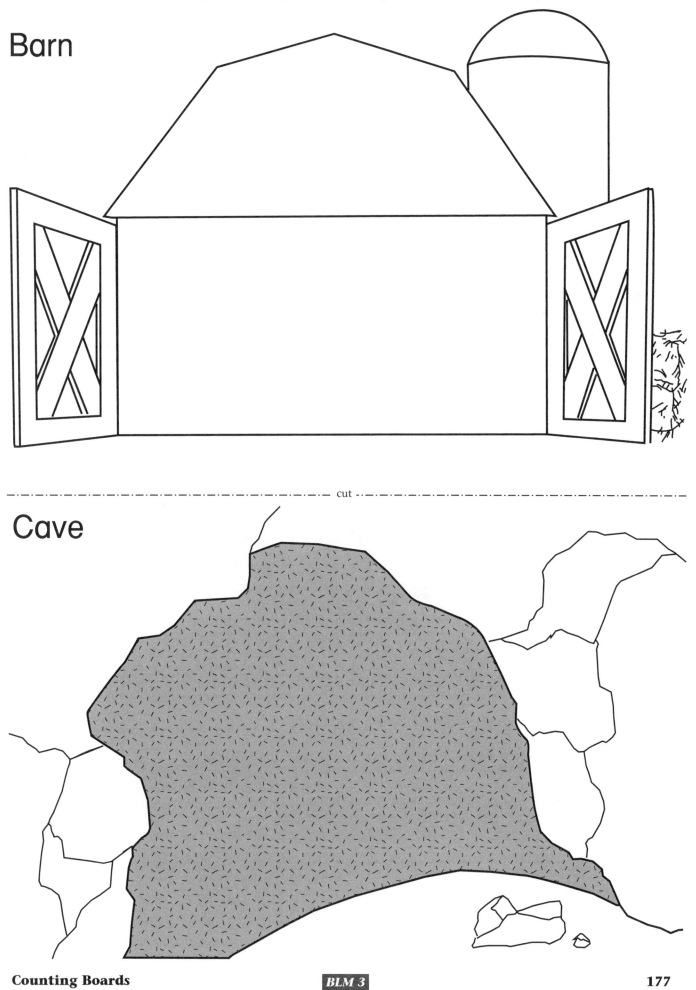

- cut -

Corral

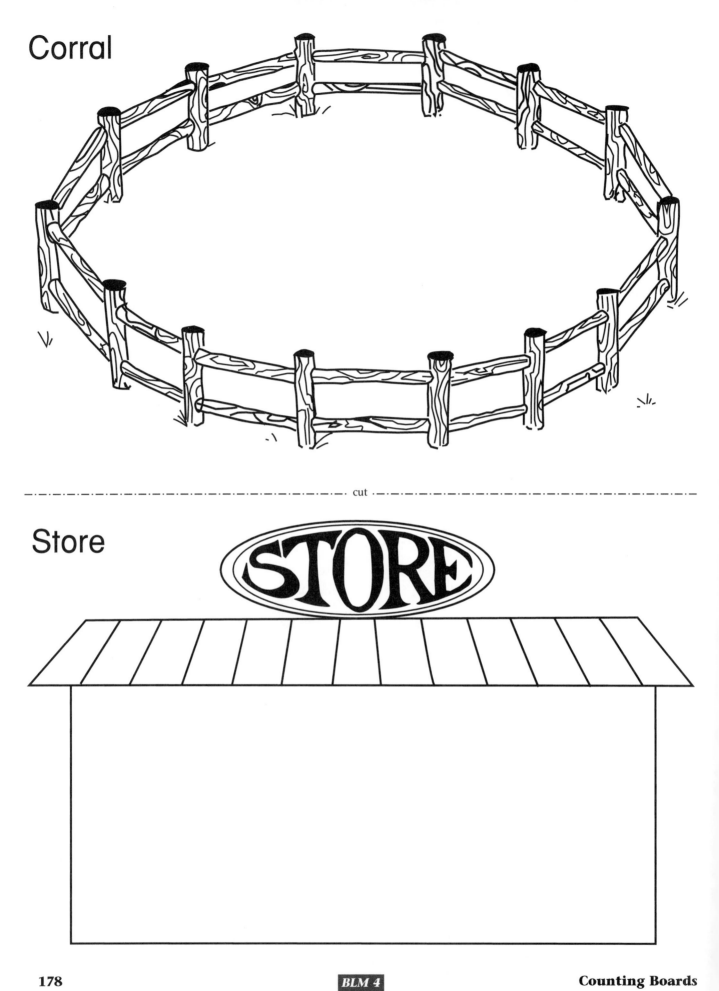

----------------------------------- cut -----------------------------------

Store

STORE

BLM 4

Counting Boards

Road

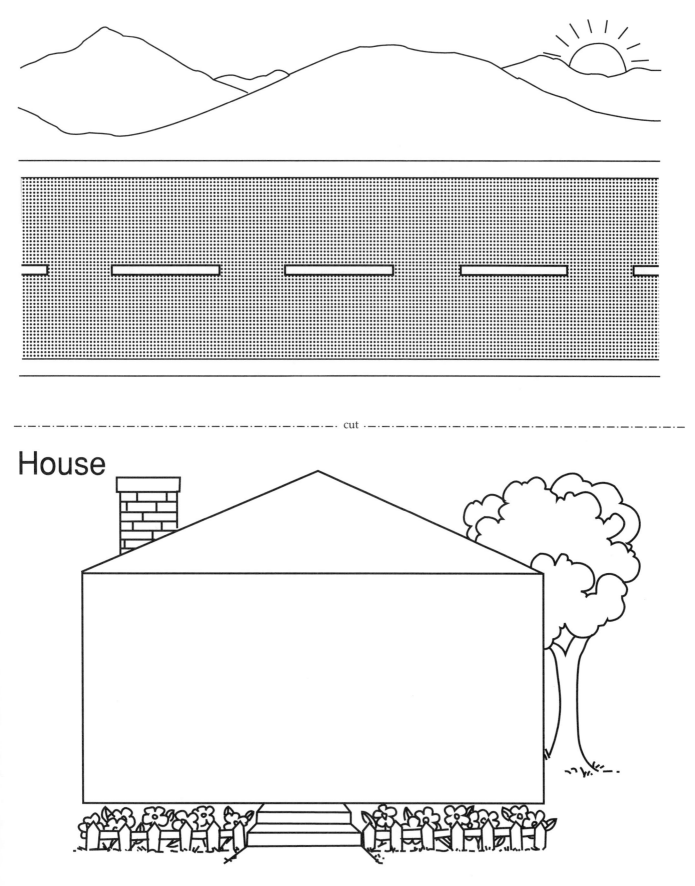

─ ─ ─ ─ ─ ─ ─ ─ ─ ─ cut ─ ─ ─ ─ ─ ─ ─ ─ ─ ─

House

Garden

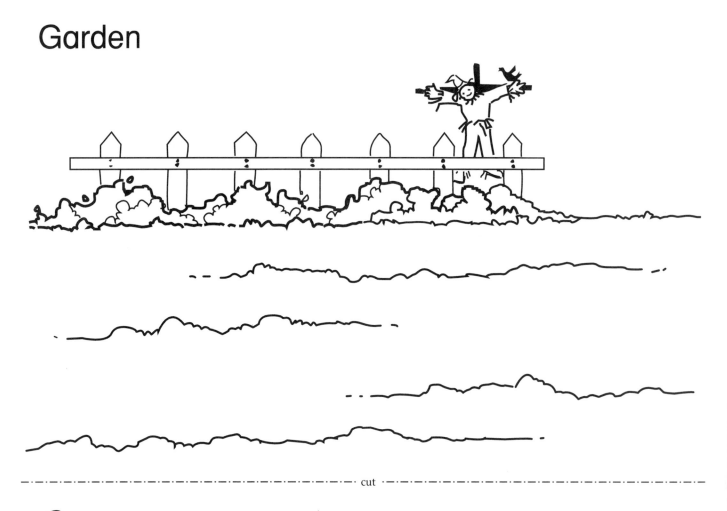

- - - cut - - -

Grass

BLM 6

Counting Boards

☺ 11   ☺ 12   ☺ 13   ☺ 14   ☺ 15

☺ 11   ☺ 12   ☺ 13   ☺ 14   ☺ 15

☺ 11   ☺ 12   ☺ 13   ☺ 14   ☺ 15

☺ 16   ☺ 17   ☺ 18   ☺ 19   ☺ 20

☺ 16   ☺ 17   ☺ 18   ☺ 19   ☺ 20

☺ 16   ☺ 17   ☺ 18   ☺ 19   ☺ 20

☺ ☺ ☺ ☺ ☺

15   *14*   *13*   *12*   *11*

☺ ☺ ☺ ☺ ☺

15   *14*   *13*   *12*   *11*

☺ ☺ ☺ ☺ ☺

15   *14*   *13*   *12*   *11*

☺ ☺ ☺ ☺ ☺

20   *19*   *18*   *17*   *16*

☺ ☺ ☺ ☺ ☺

20   *19*   *18*   *17*   *16*

☺ ☺ ☺ ☺ ☺

20   *19*   *18*   *17*   *16*

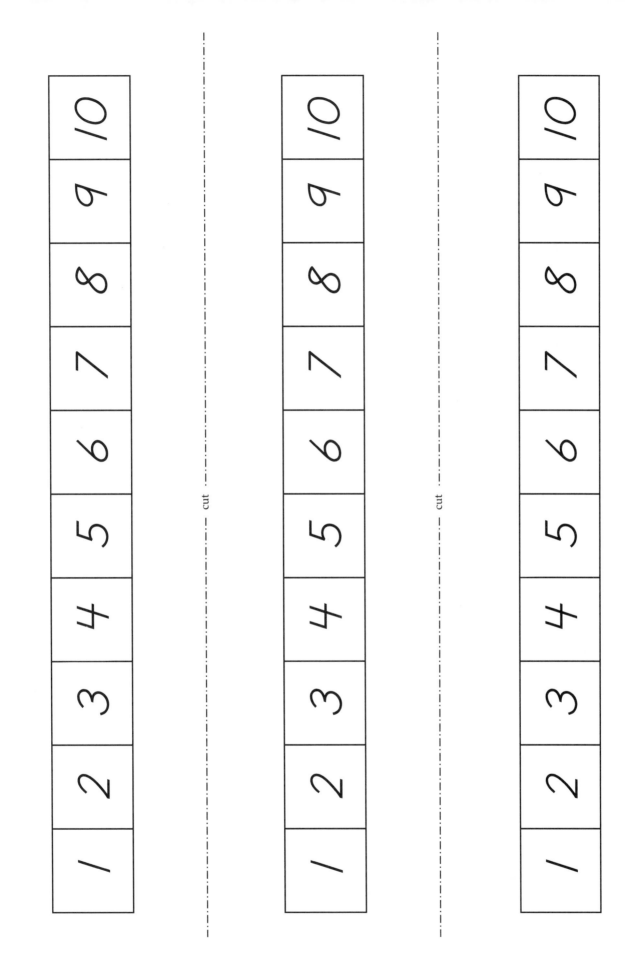

| 1 | 2 | 3 | 4 | 5 | 6 | 7 | 8 | 9 | 10 |

cut

| 1 | 2 | 3 | 4 | 5 | 6 | 7 | 8 | 9 | 10 |

cut

| 1 | 2 | 3 | 4 | 5 | 6 | 7 | 8 | 9 | 10 |

1	2	3	4	5	6	7	8	9	10
11	12	13	14	15	16	17	18	19	20

cut

1	2	3	4	5	6	7	8	9	10
11	12	13	14	15	16	17	18	19	20

cut

1	2	3	4	5	6	7	8	9	10
11	12	13	14	15	16	17	18	19	20

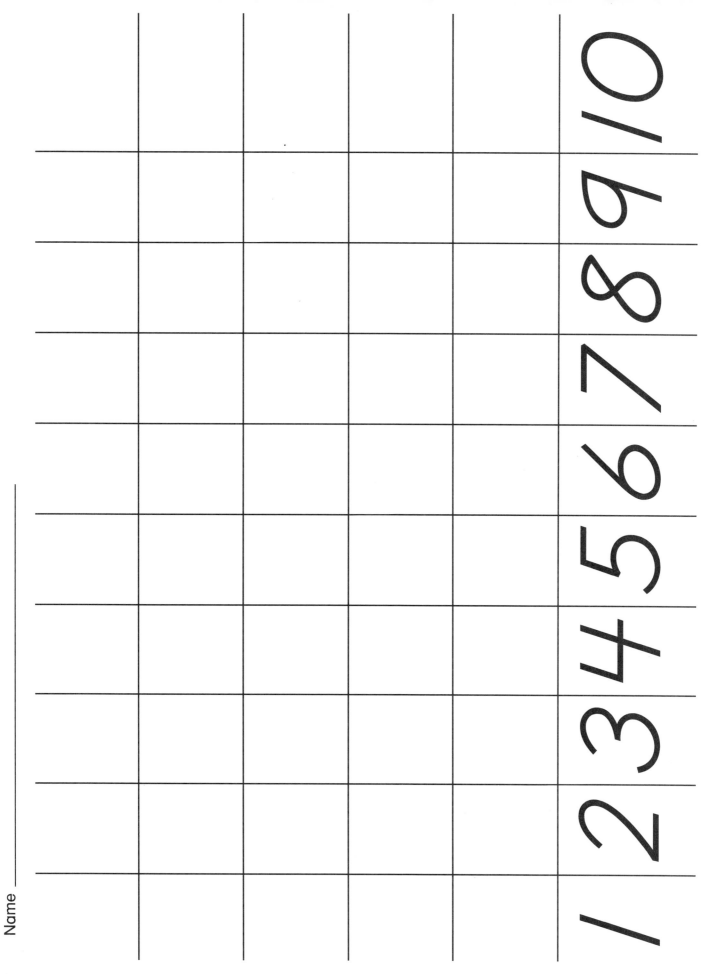

Name _____

Shape Puzzles (3–6)

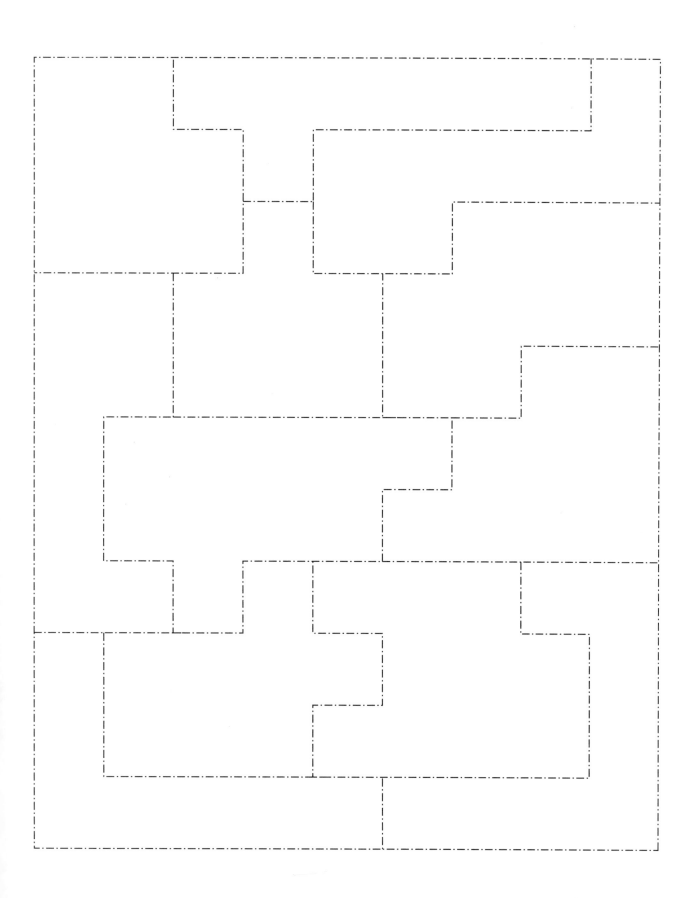

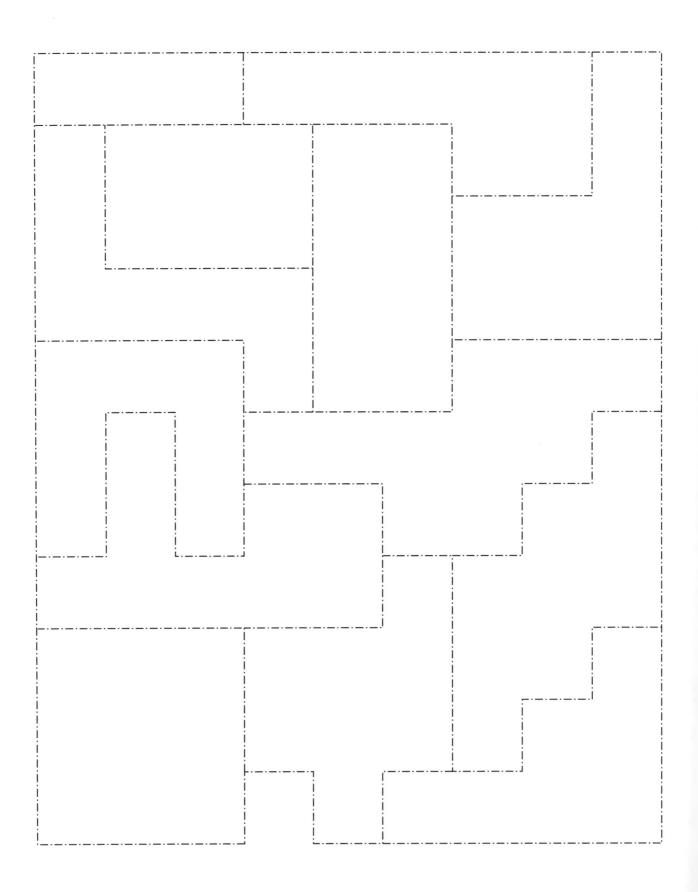

BLM 36

Shape Puzzles (7–10)

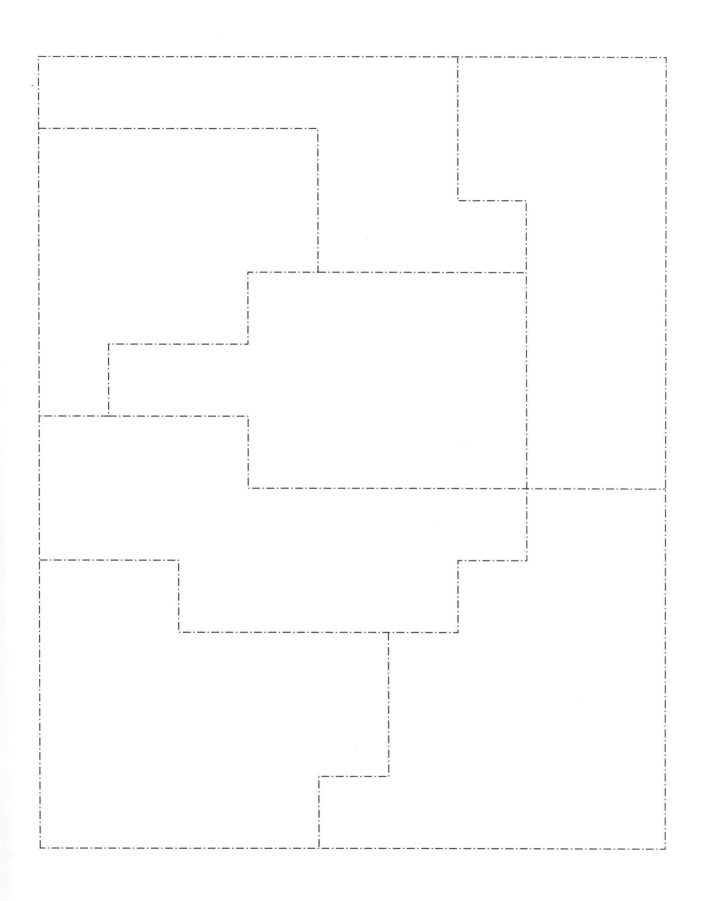

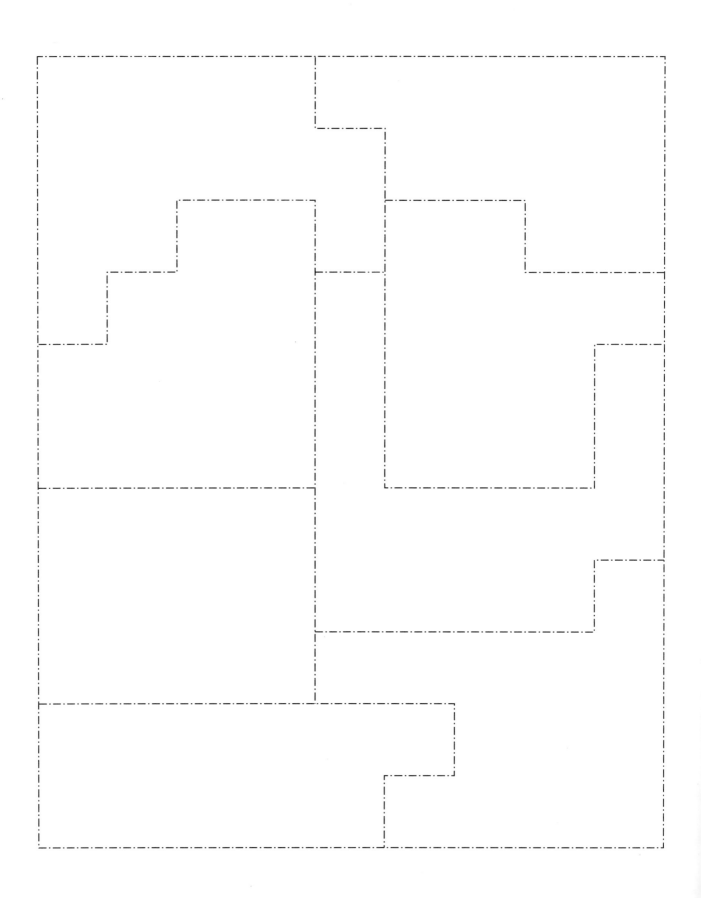

 Shape Puzzles (10–20)

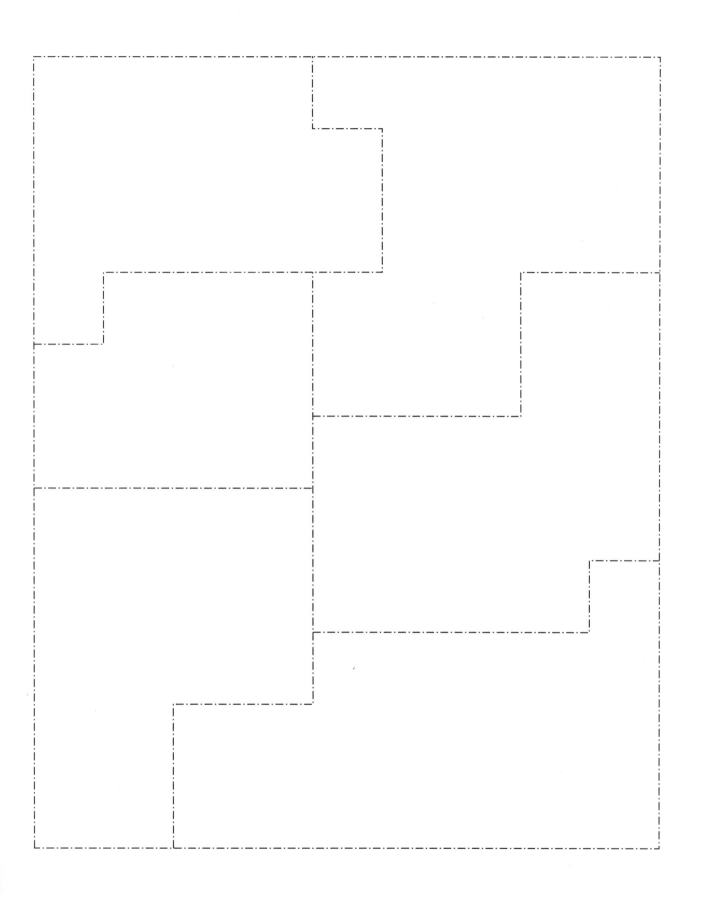

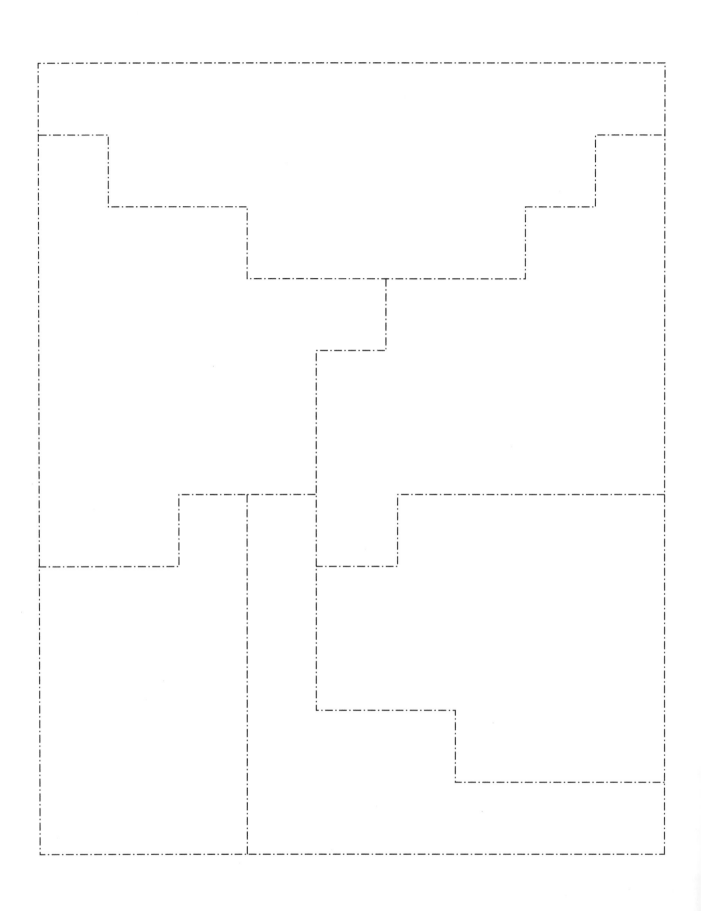

BLM 40

Shape Puzzles (10–20)

cut

cut

1 + 0	4 + 0	1 + 4
0 + 1	3 + 1	0 + 5
2 + 0	2 + 2	6 + 0
1 + 1	1 + 2	5 + 1
0 + 2	0 + 4	4 + 2
3 + 0	5 + 0	3 + 3
2 + 1	4 + 1	2 + 4
1 + 2	3 + 2	1 + 5
0 + 3	2 + 3	0 + 6

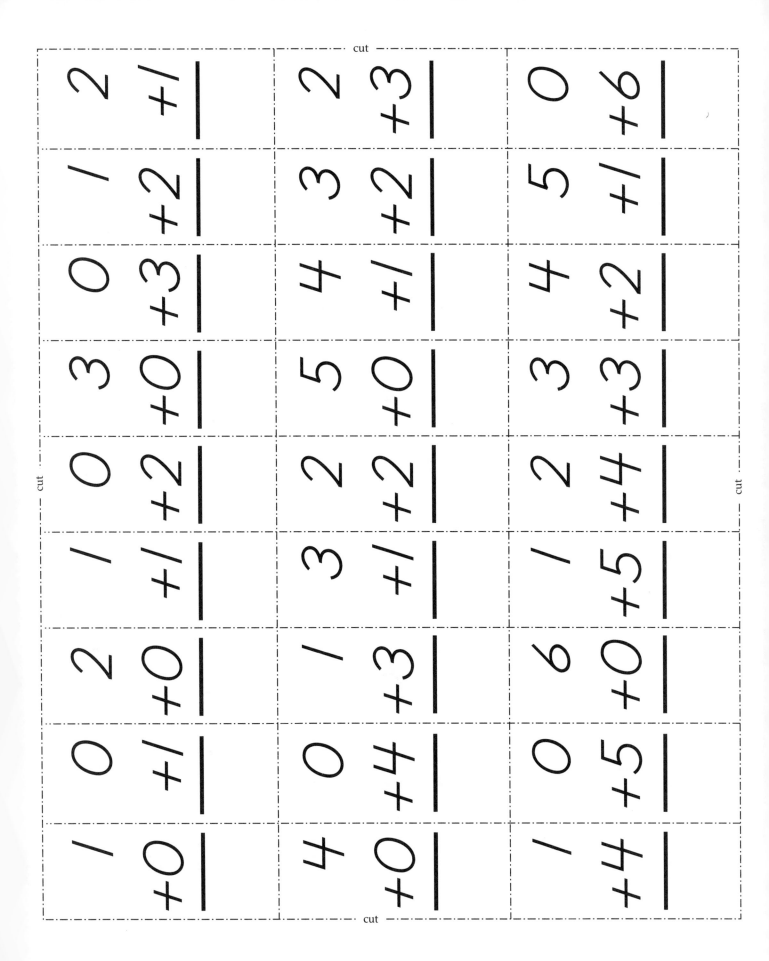

2 +1	2 +3	0 +6
1 +2	3 +2	5 +1
0 +3	4 +1	4 +2
3 +0	5 +0	3 +3
0 +2	2 +2	2 +4
1 +1	3 +1	1 +5
2 +0	1 +3	6 +0
0 +1	0 +4	0 +5
1 +0	4 +0	1 +4

cut

7 + 0	7 + 1	8 + 1
6 + 1	6 + 2	7 + 2
5 + 2	5 + 3	6 + 3
4 + 3	4 + 4	5 + 4
3 + 4	3 + 5	4 + 5
2 + 5	2 + 6	3 + 6
1 + 6	1 + 7	2 + 7
0 + 7	0 + 8	1 + 8
8 + 0	9 + 0	0 + 9

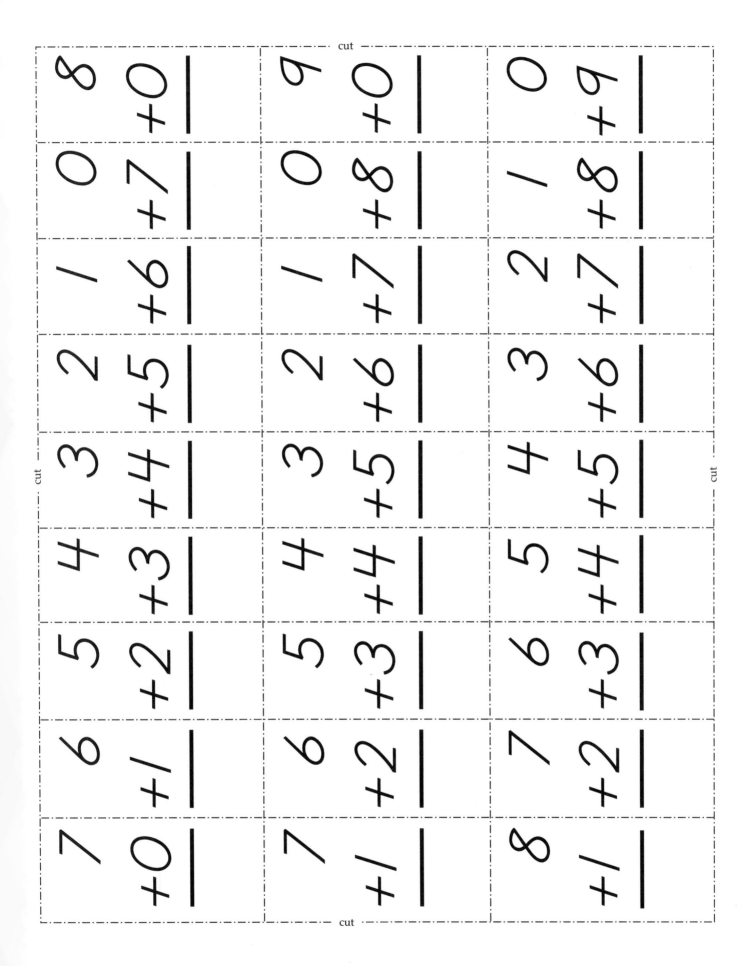

8
+0

9
+0

0
+9

0
+7

0
+8

1
+8

1
+6

1
+7

2
+7

2
+5

2
+6

3
+6

3
+4

3
+5

4
+5

4
+3

4
+4

5
+4

5
+2

5
+3

6
+3

6
+1

6
+2

7
+2

7
+0

7
+1

8
+1

cut

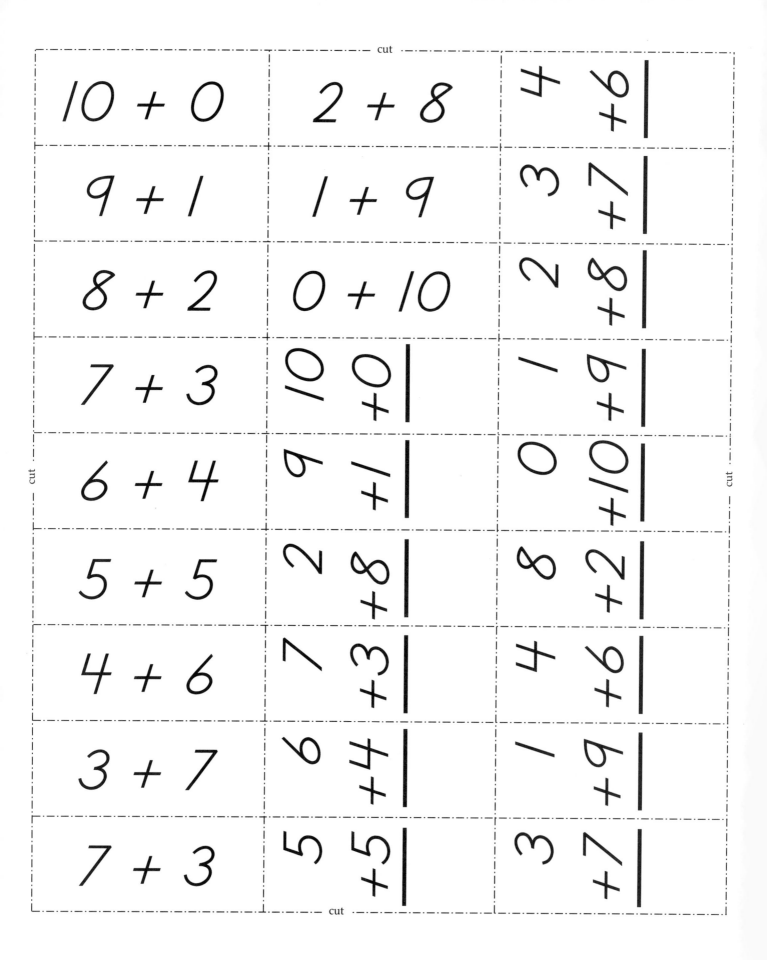

BLM 68

Addition Cards (Sums of 10)

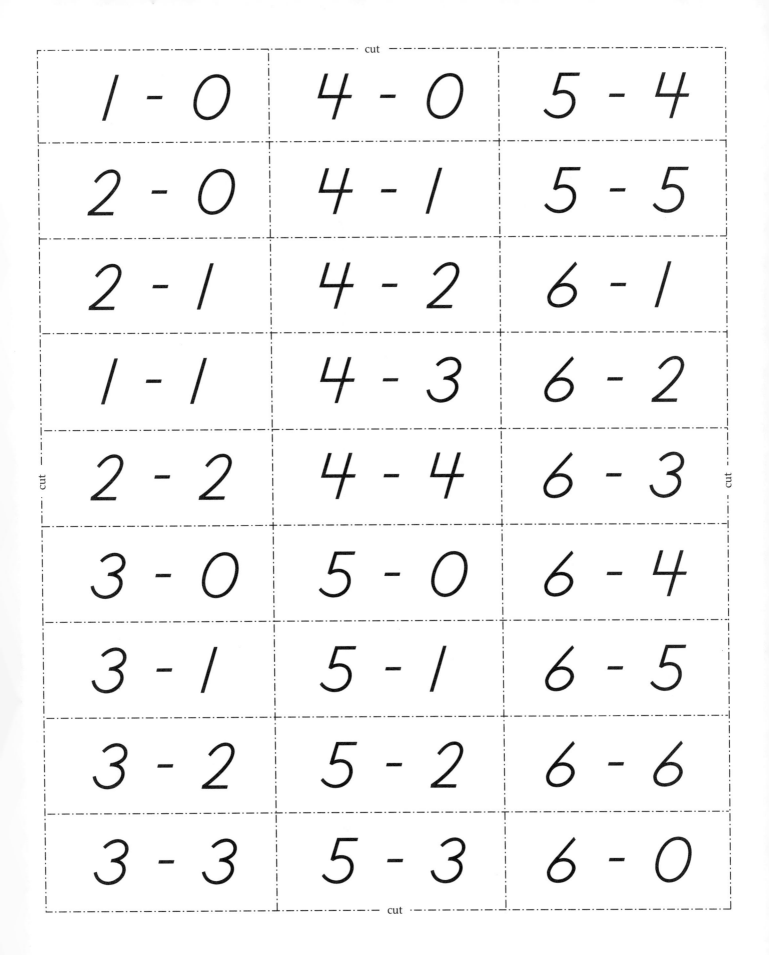

1 - 0	4 - 0	5 - 4
2 - 0	4 - 1	5 - 5
2 - 1	4 - 2	6 - 1
1 - 1	4 - 3	6 - 2
2 - 2	4 - 4	6 - 3
3 - 0	5 - 0	6 - 4
3 - 1	5 - 1	6 - 5
3 - 2	5 - 2	6 - 6
3 - 3	5 - 3	6 - 0

Subtraction Cards (Subtracting from 1 to 6) *BLM 69*   199

3	3	6
−3	−3	−6

3	5	6
−2	−2	−5

3	5	6
−1	−1	−4

3	5	6
−0	−0	−3

2	4	6
−2	−4	−2

2	4	6
−1	−3	−1

2	4	6
−0	−2	−0

1	4	5
−1	−1	−5

1	4	5
−0	−0	−4

BLM 70 Subtraction Cards (Subtracting from 1 to 6)

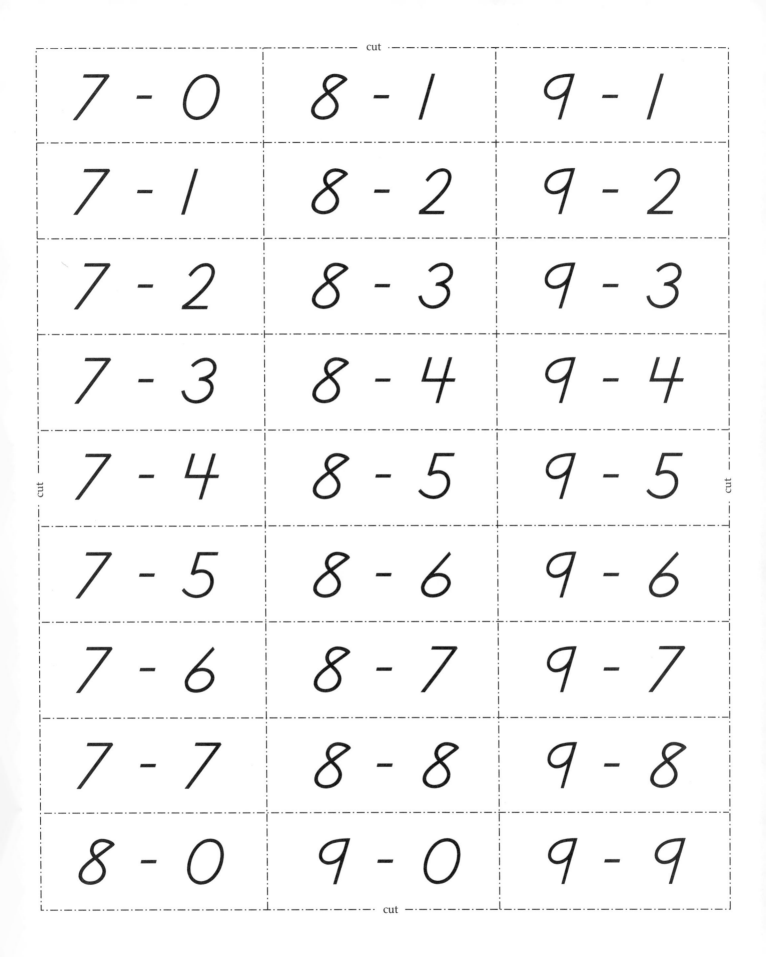

7 - 0	8 - 1	9 - 1
7 - 1	8 - 2	9 - 2
7 - 2	8 - 3	9 - 3
7 - 3	8 - 4	9 - 4
7 - 4	8 - 5	9 - 5
7 - 5	8 - 6	9 - 6
7 - 6	8 - 7	9 - 7
7 - 7	8 - 8	9 - 8
8 - 0	9 - 0	9 - 9

Subtraction Cards (Subtracting from 7 to 9)   BLM 71   201

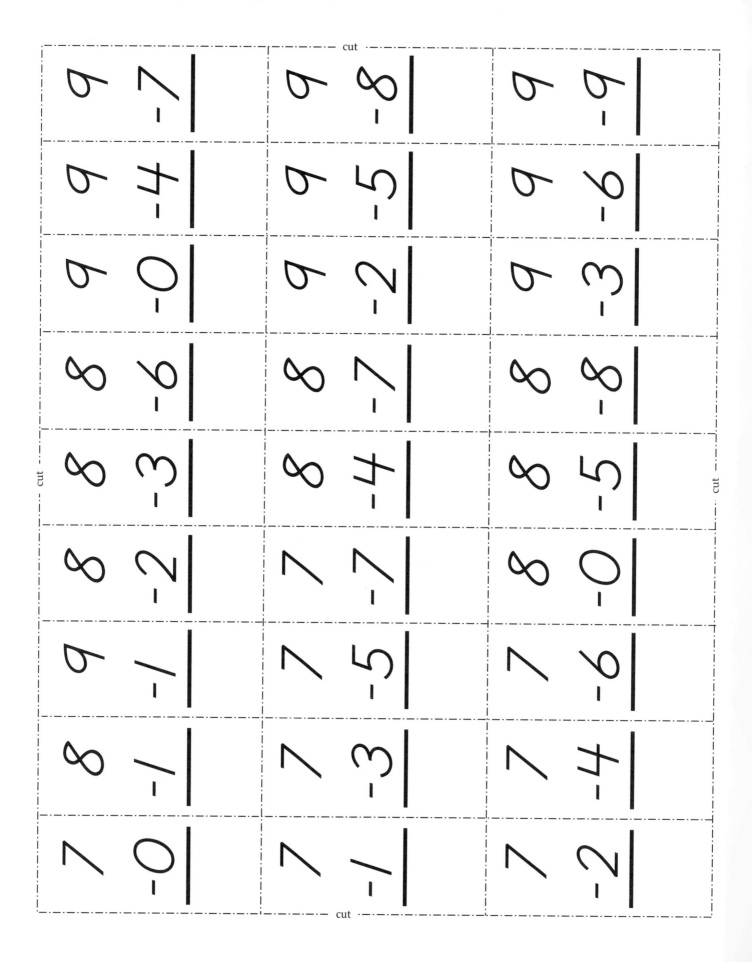

BLM 72 **Subtraction Cards (Subtracting from 7 to 9)**

10 - 0	10 - 9	10 - 7
10 - 1	10 - 10	10 - 8
10 - 2	10 - 0	10 - 9
10 - 3	10 - 1	10 -10
10 - 4	10 - 2	10 - 2
10 - 5	10 - 3	10 - 4
10 - 6	10 - 4	10 - 6
10 - 7	10 - 5	10 - 7
10 - 8	10 - 6	10 - 8

BLM 74

Clear-the-Deck Game Board

The Hiding Assessment

The child determines the missing parts of numbers (up to 10) when shown one part.

Child's Name _____

Observations

Assessment Procedures	Date _____	Date _____	Date _____	Date _____
Ask the child to hand you a particular number of counters. When assessing a child for the first time, ask the child to hand you five counters. Hide some of the counters in one hand and show the child the remaining counters in your other hand. Ask, "How many are hiding?" Change the number of counters that you are "hiding" and ask, "Now, how many are hiding?" Repeat for several combinations for that number. If the child is successful with the number you are assessing, check larger numbers in the same way. If the child is unsuccessful with that number, check smaller numbers.	**Number** _____ ____ Makes no response or says, "I don't know." ____ Says an unreasonable number. ____ Tells a number that is close but inaccurate. ____ Figures out how many are hiding. ____ Knows quickly and confidently. **Number** _____ ____ Makes no response or says, "I don't know." ____ Says an unreasonable number. ____ Tells a number that is close but inaccurate. ____ Figures out how many are hiding. ____ Knows quickly and confidently.	**Number** _____ ____ Makes no response or says, "I don't know." ____ Says an unreasonable number. ____ Tells a number that is close but inaccurate. ____ Figures out how many are hiding. ____ Knows quickly and confidently. **Number** _____ ____ Makes no response or says, "I don't know." ____ Says an unreasonable number. ____ Tells a number that is close but inaccurate. ____ Figures out how many are hiding. ____ Knows quickly and confidently.	**Number** _____ ____ Makes no response or says, "I don't know." ____ Says an unreasonable number. ____ Tells a number that is close but inaccurate. ____ Figures out how many are hiding. ____ Knows quickly and confidently. **Number** _____ ____ Makes no response or says, "I don't know." ____ Says an unreasonable number. ____ Tells a number that is close but inaccurate. ____ Figures out how many are hiding. ____ Knows quickly and confidently.	

Hiding Assessment Recording Sheet   BLM 75   205

cut

cut

BLM 76

Number Shapes (4)

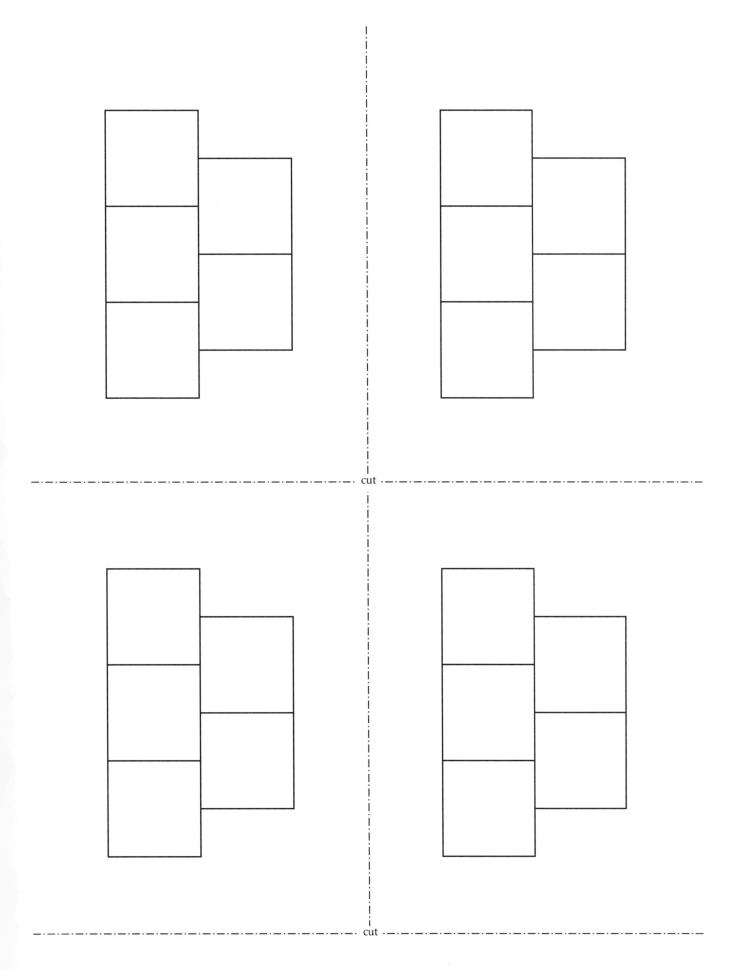

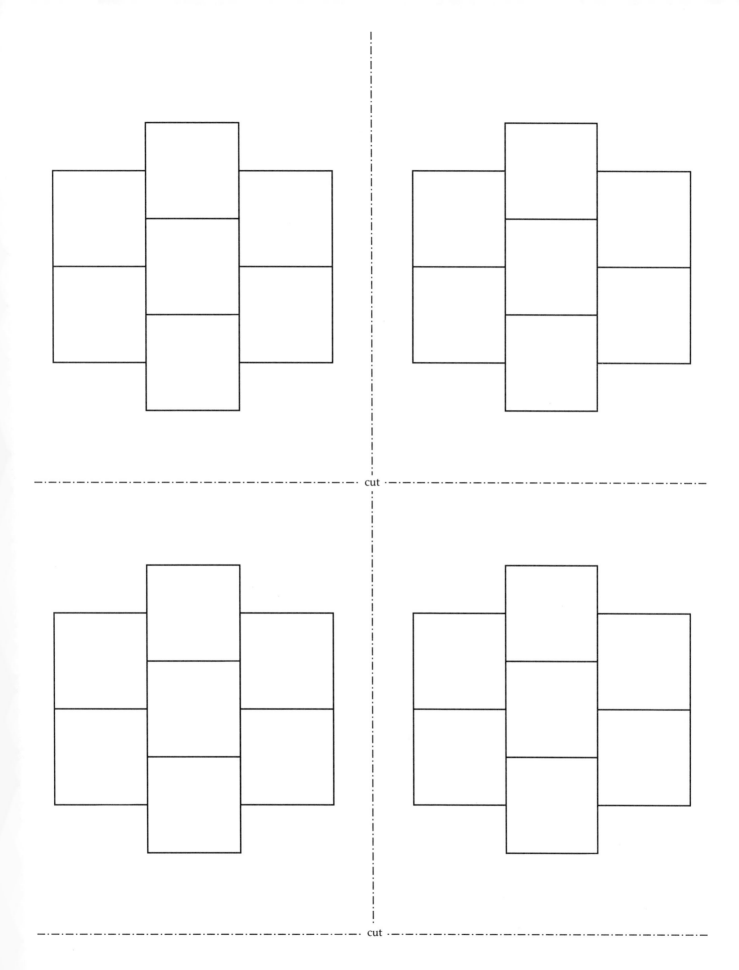

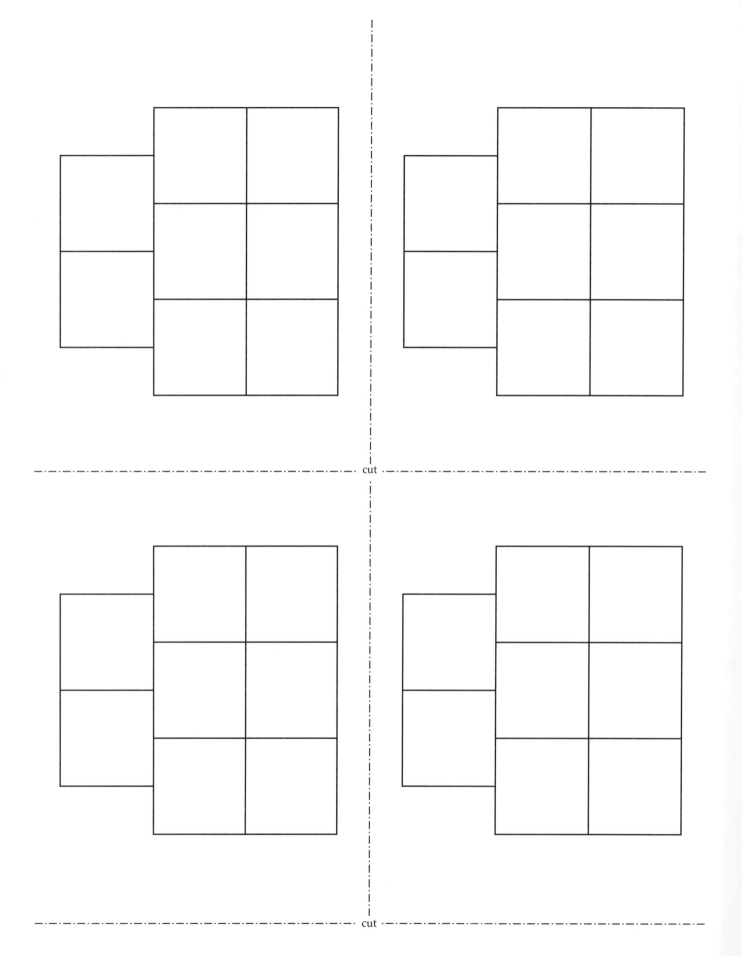

cut

cut

Number Shapes (8)

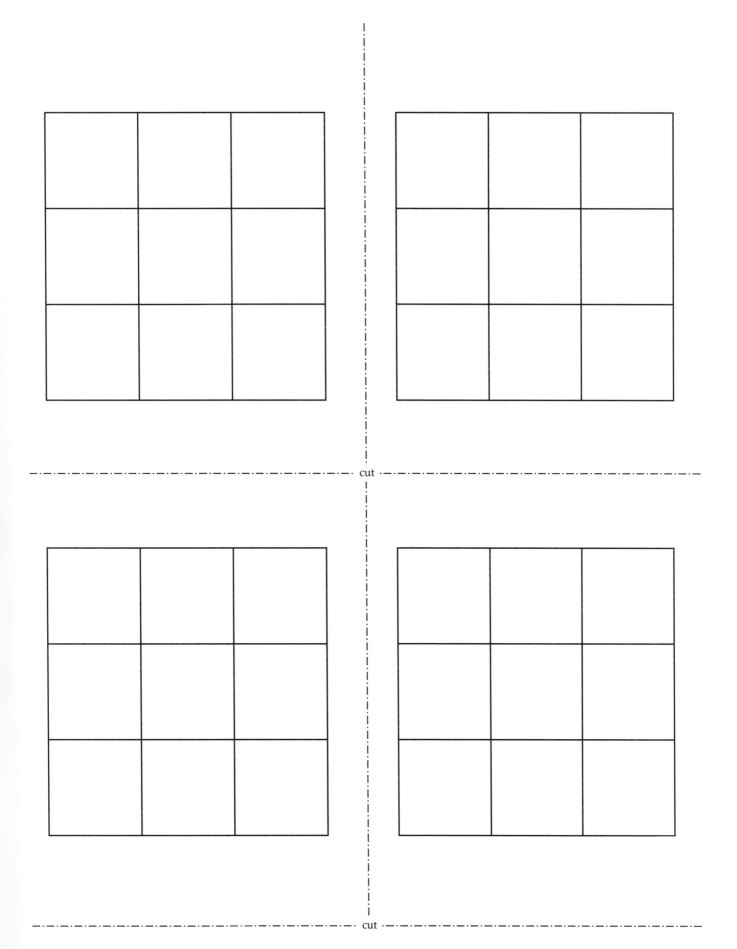

- - - - cut - - - -

- - - - cut - - - -

- - - - cut - - - -

- - - - cut - - - -

BLM 82

Number Shapes (10)

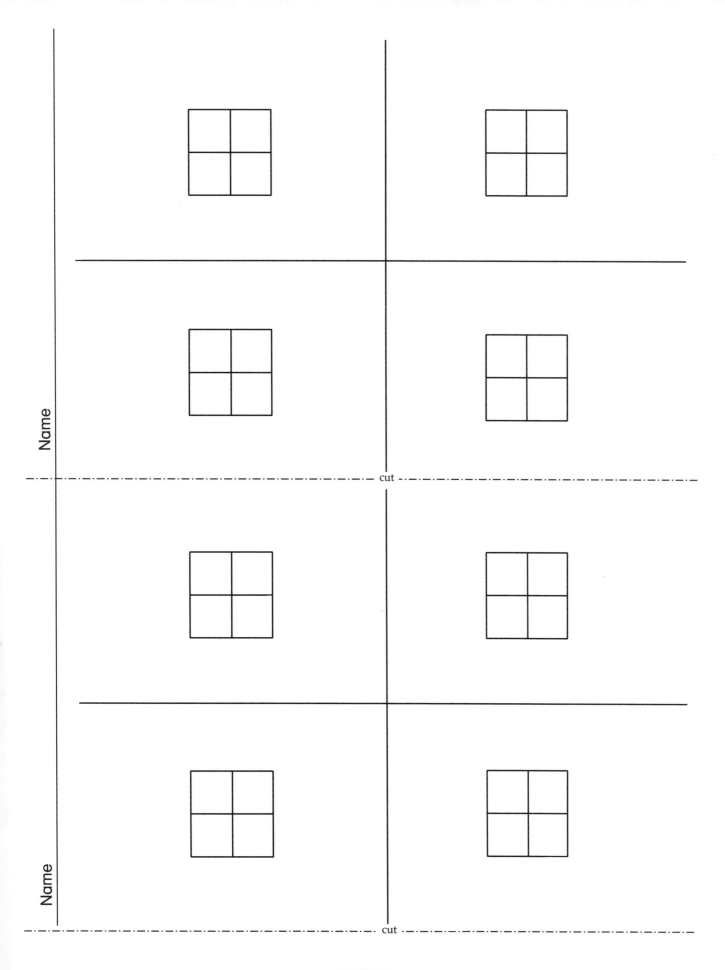

Name

Name

cut

cut

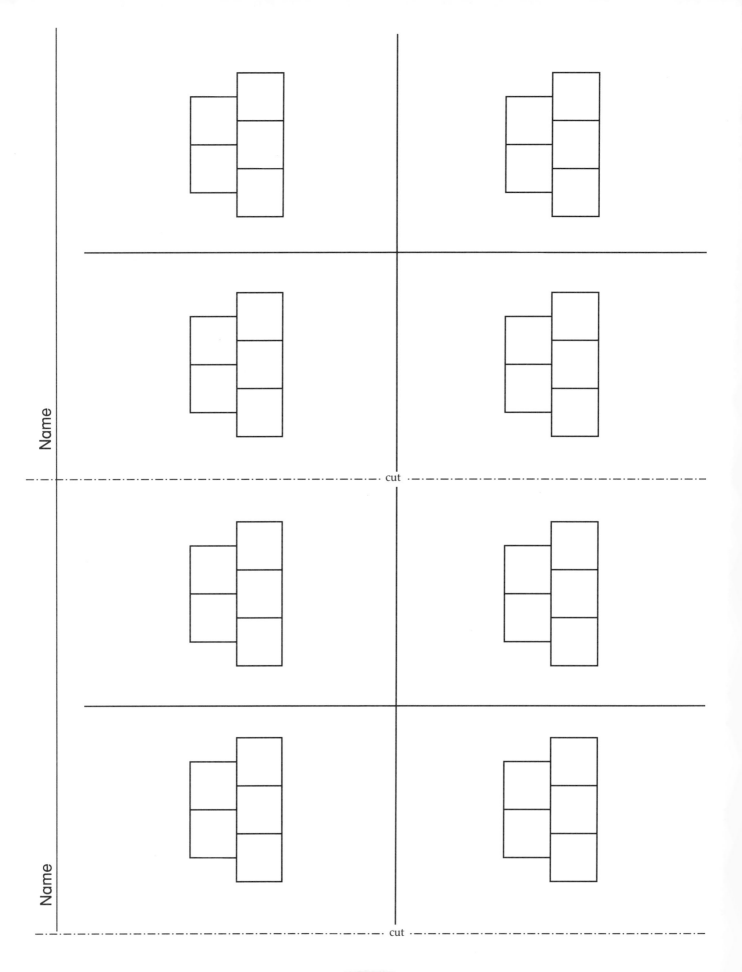

BLM 84

Number Shapes Recording Sheet (5)

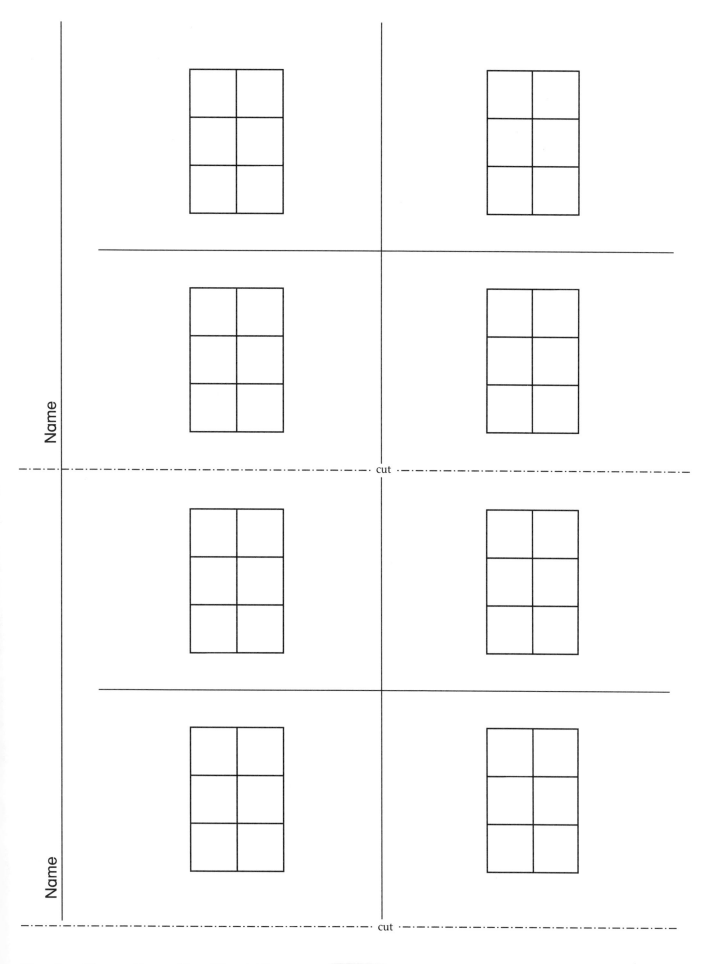

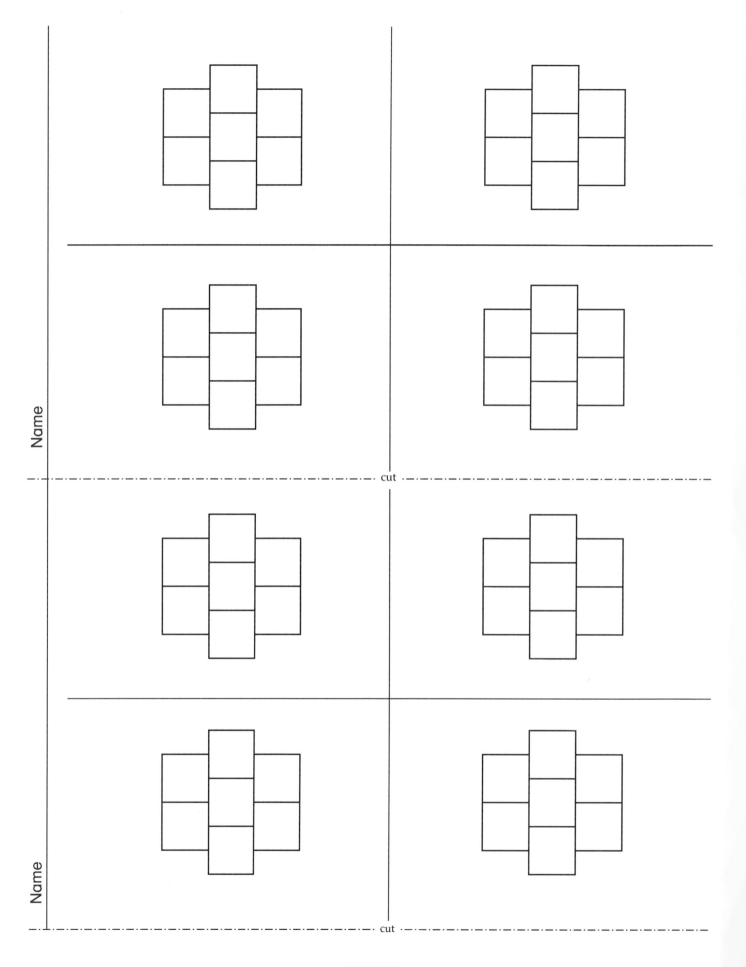

BLM 86

Number Shapes Recording Sheet (7)

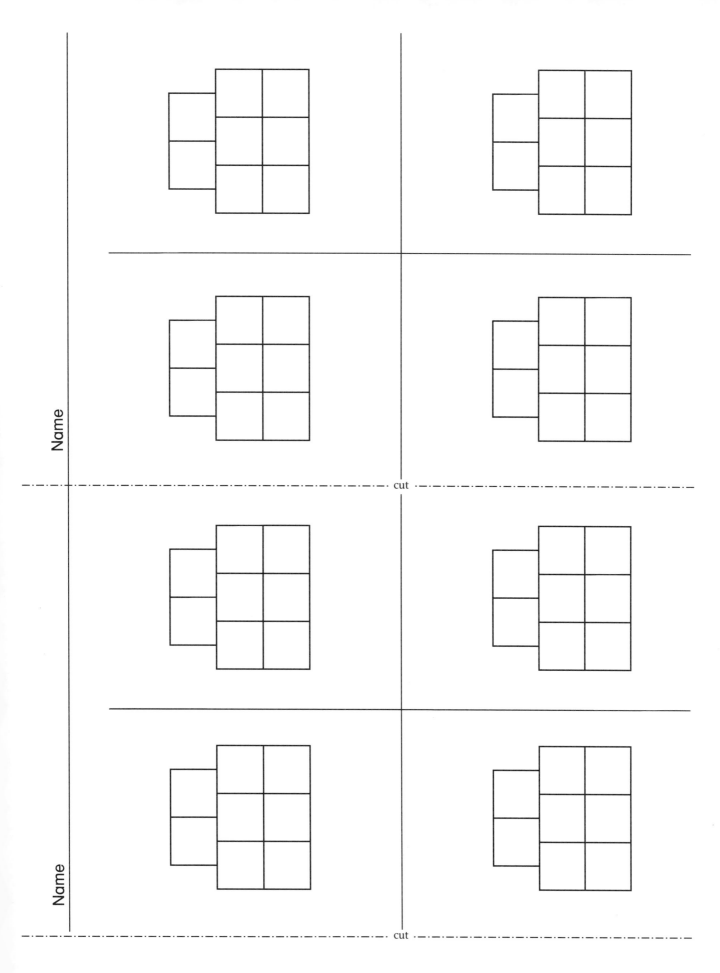

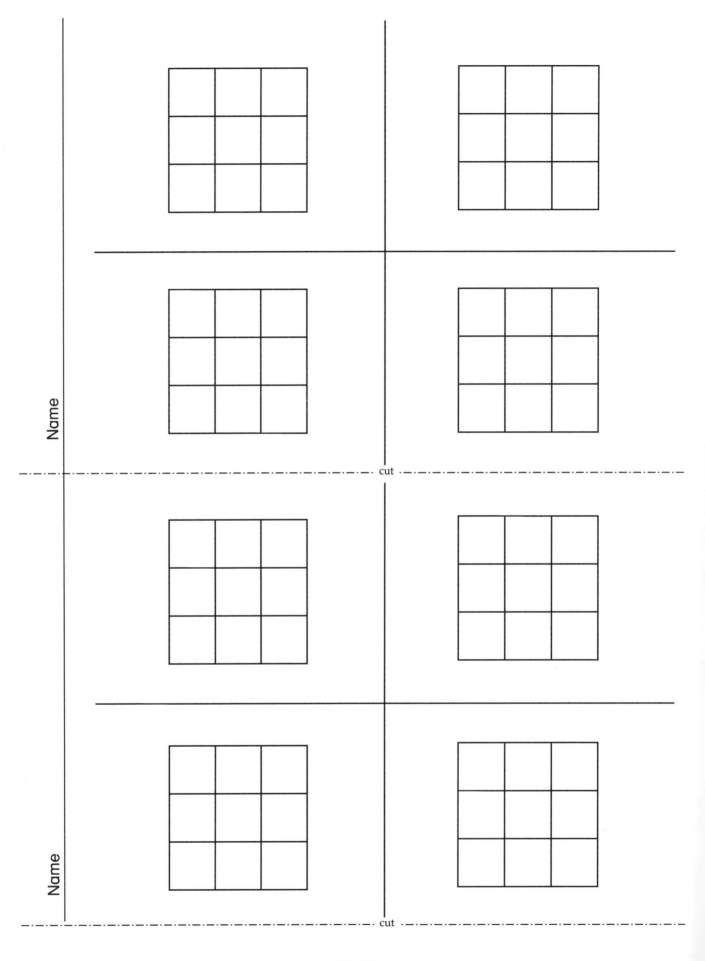

Name

Name

BLM 88

Number Shapes Recording Sheet (9)

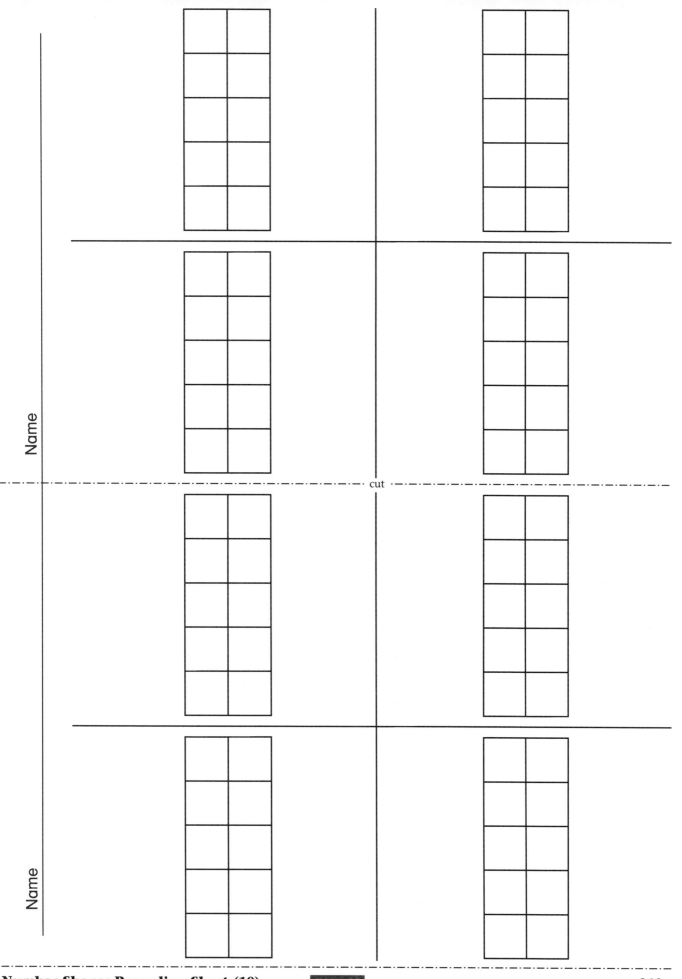

Name

Name

I worked with this number shape.

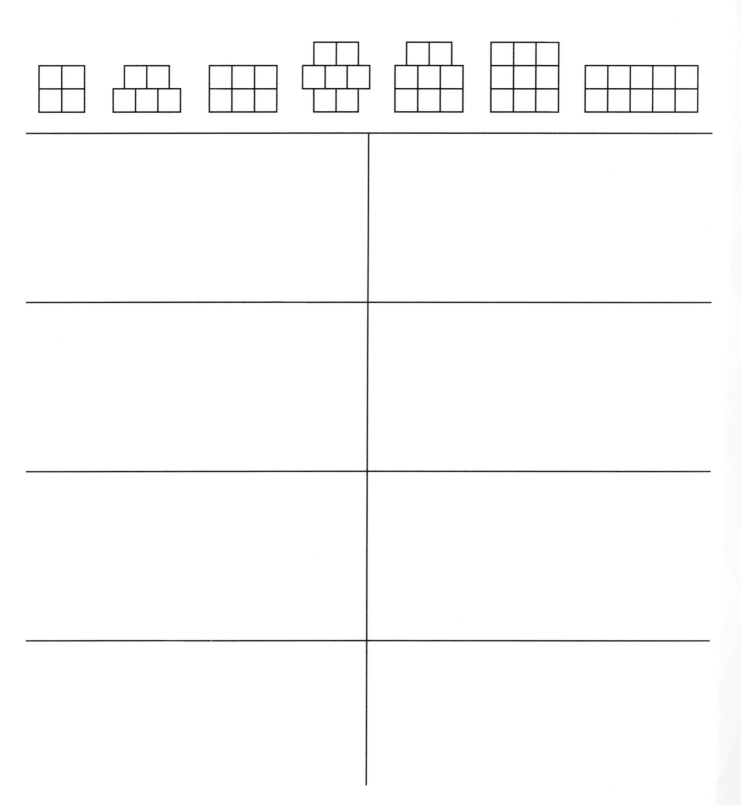

  Number Shapes Equations Worksheet

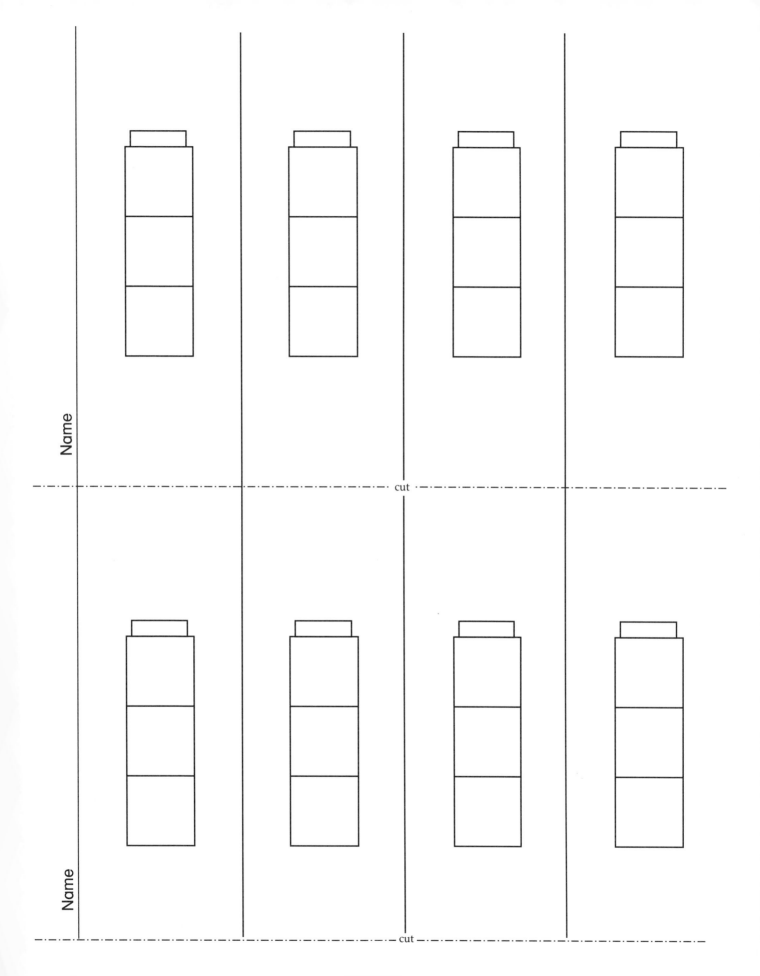

Name

cut

Name

cut

Number-Train Outlines (3)   **BLM 91**   **221**

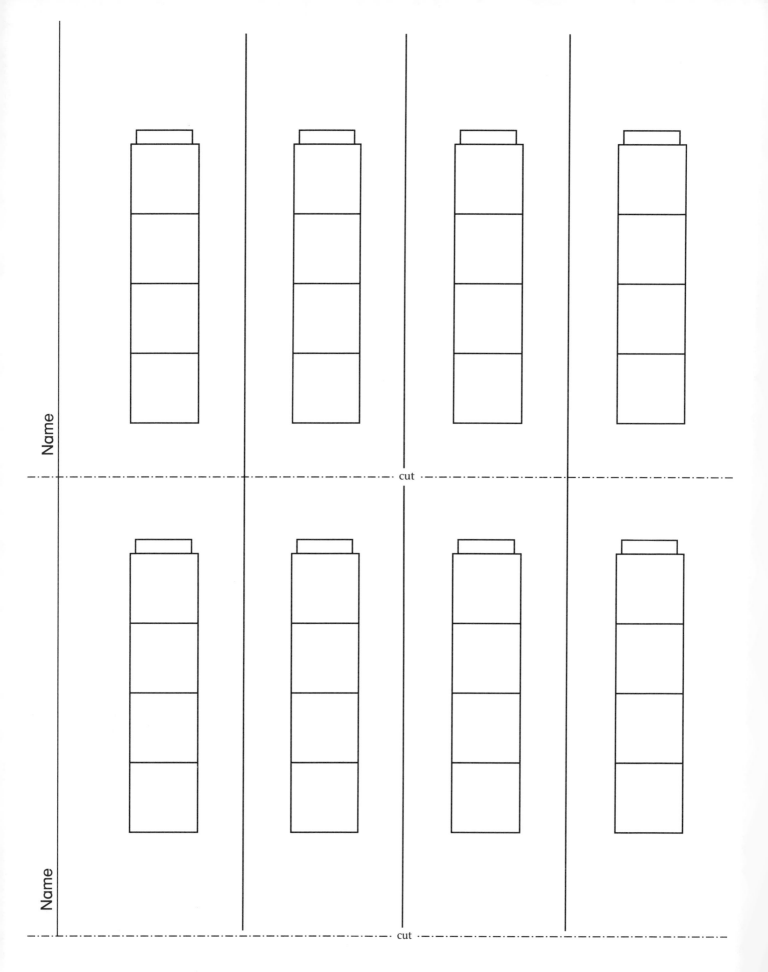

Name

cut

Name

cut

BLM 92

Number-Train Outlines (4)

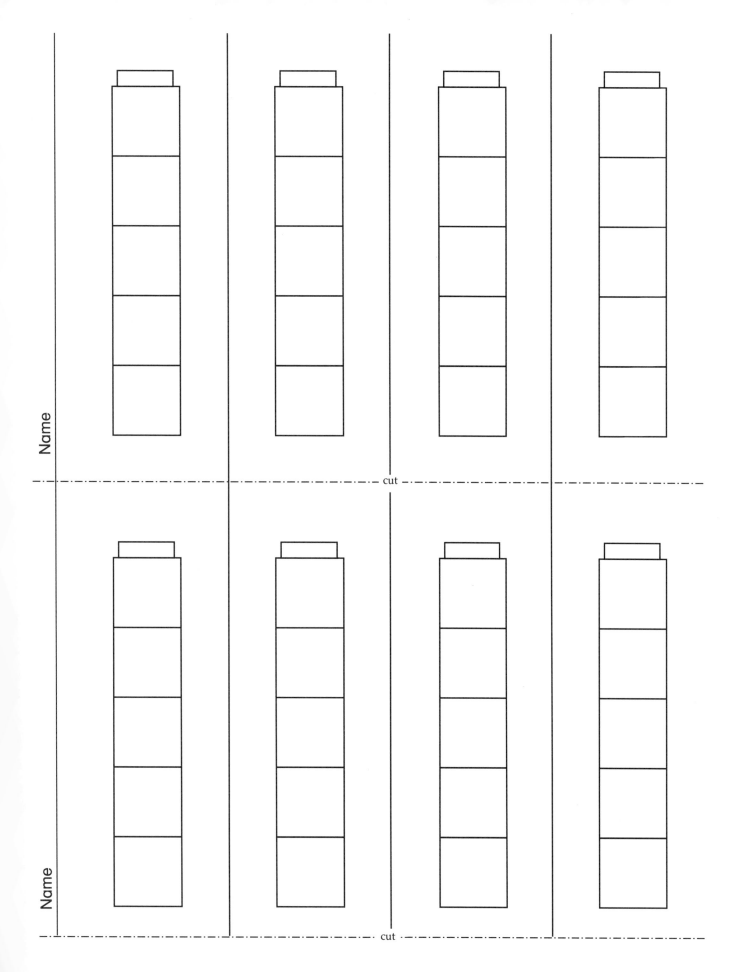

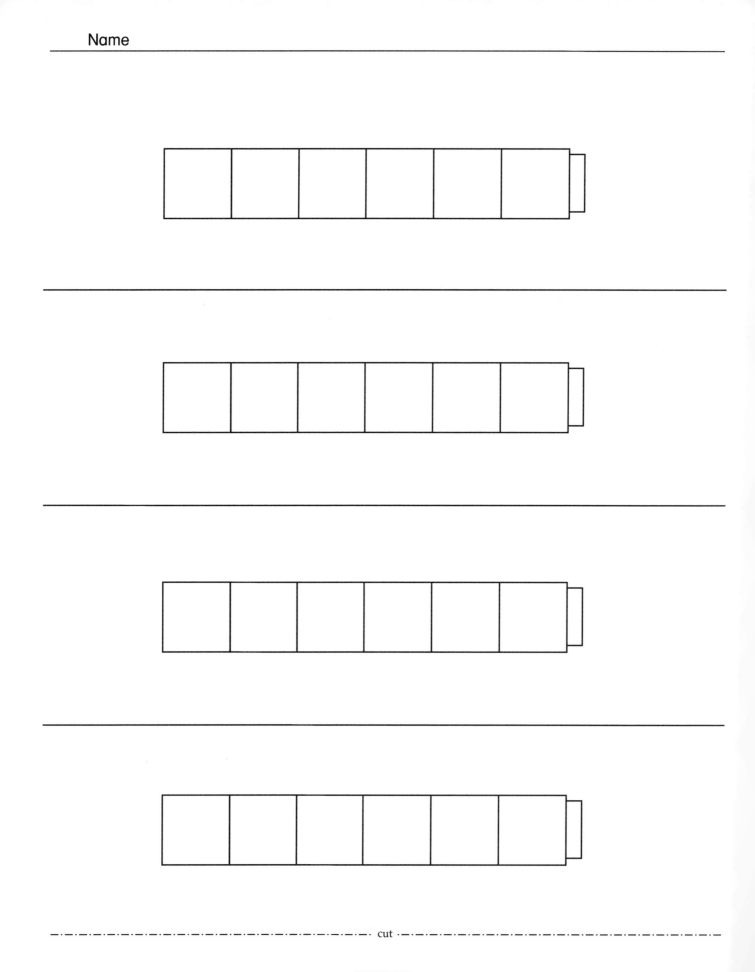

 cut

BLM 94   **Number-Train Outlines (6)**

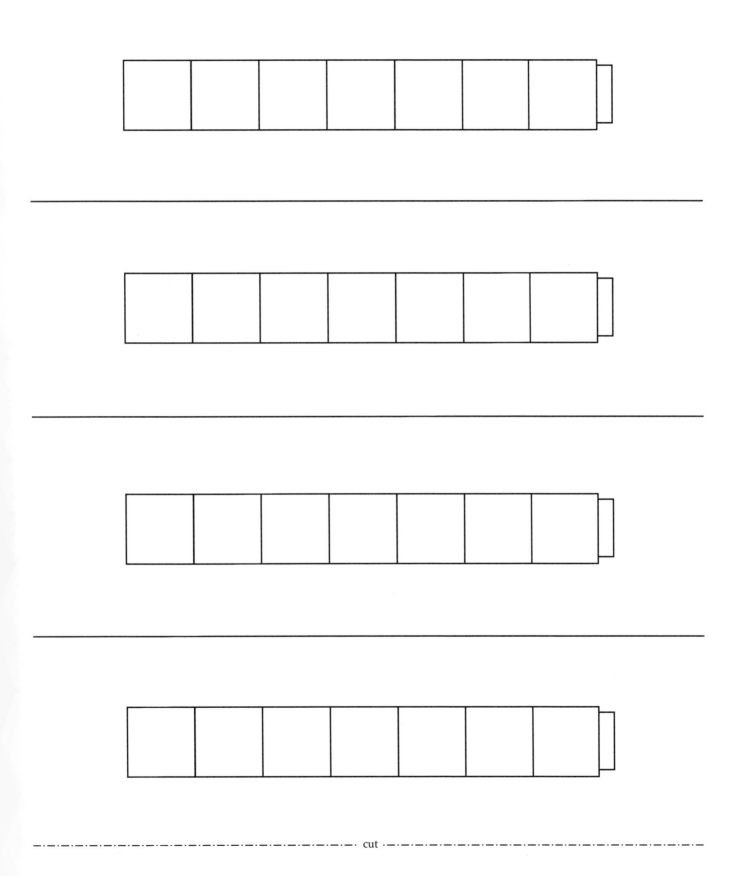

- cut -

Name _____

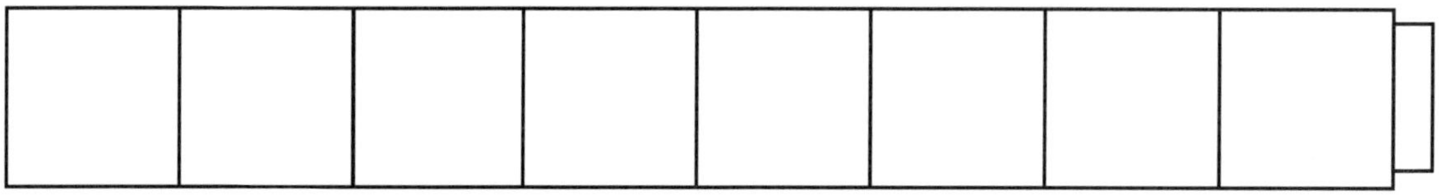

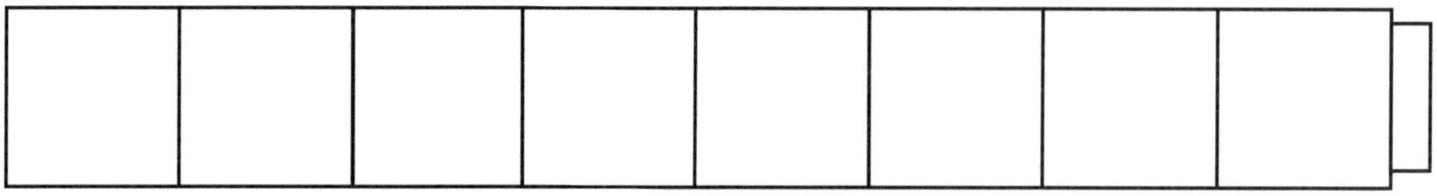

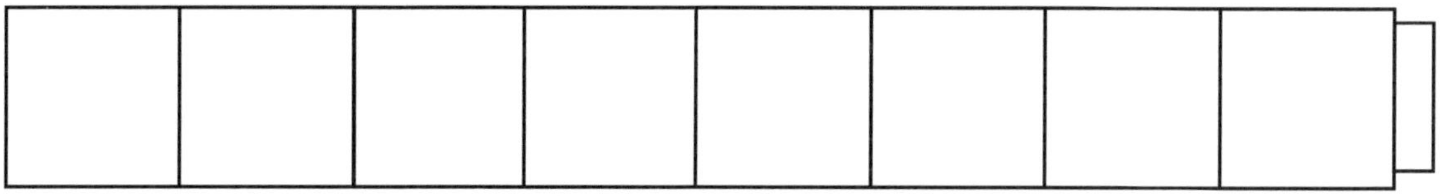

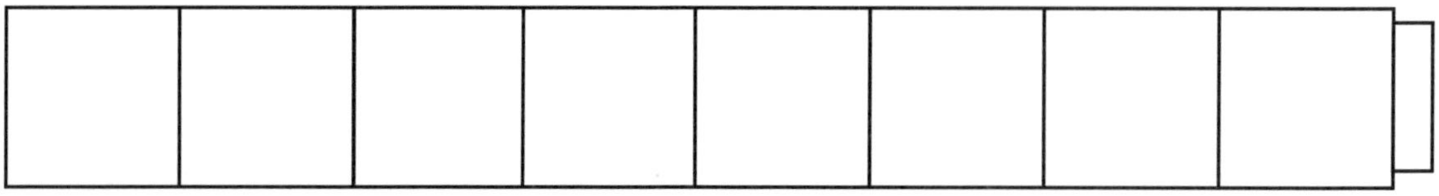

BLM 96

Number-Train Outlines (8)

Name _____

- - - cut - - -

Number-Train Outlines (9)   BLM 97   227

BLM 98

Number-Train Outlines (10)

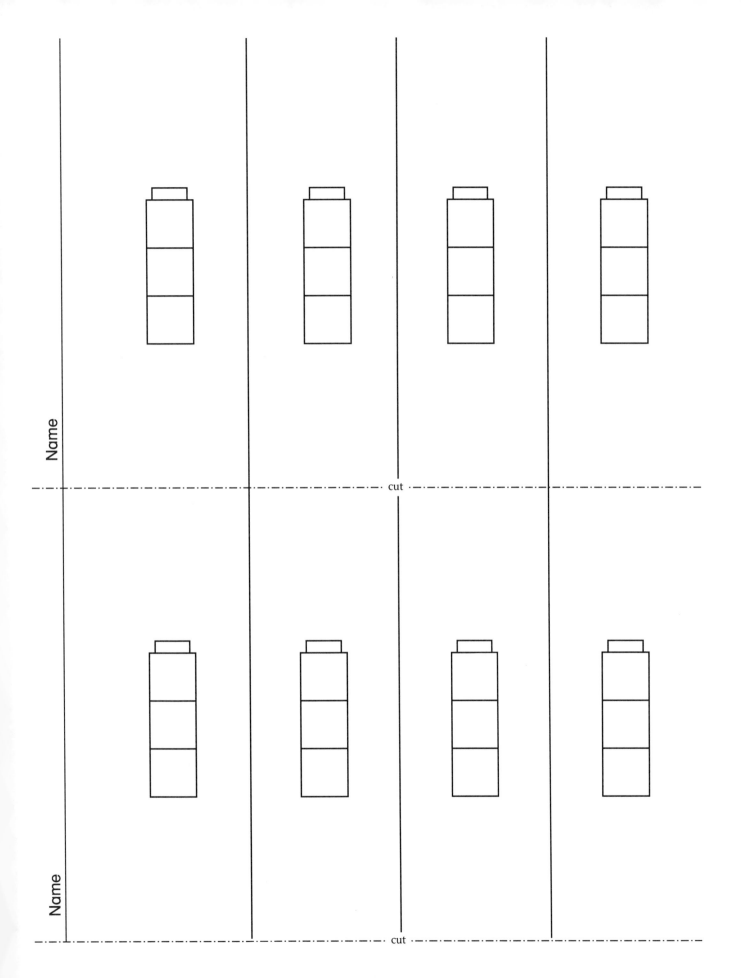

Name

- - - cut - - -

Name

- - - cut - - -

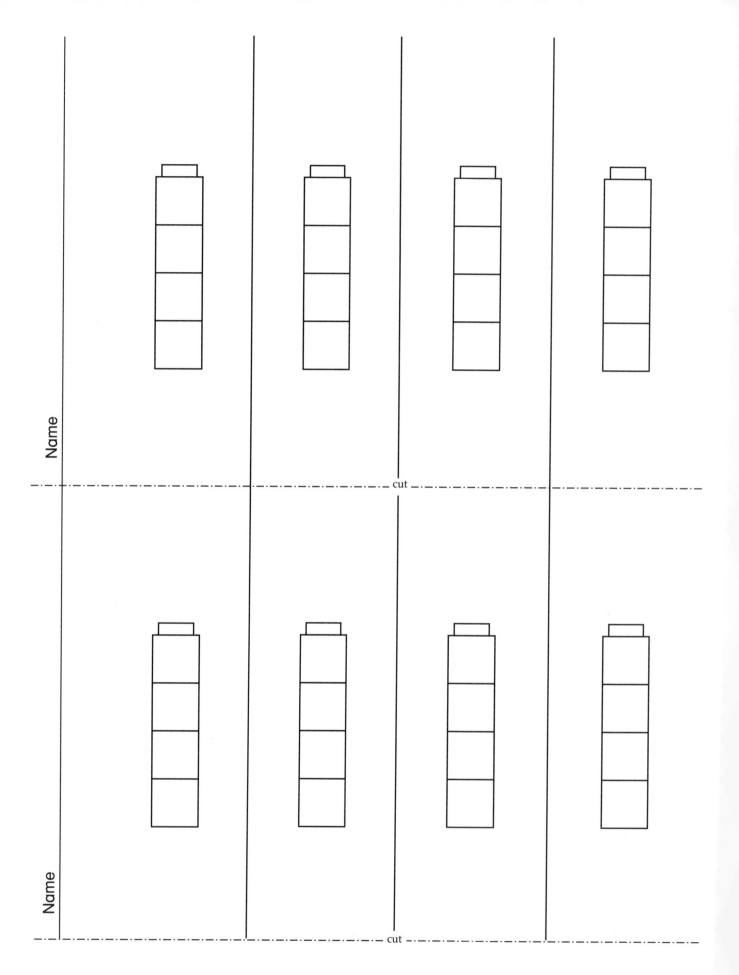

Name

cut

Name

cut

BLM 100   **Number Trains Recording Sheet (4)**

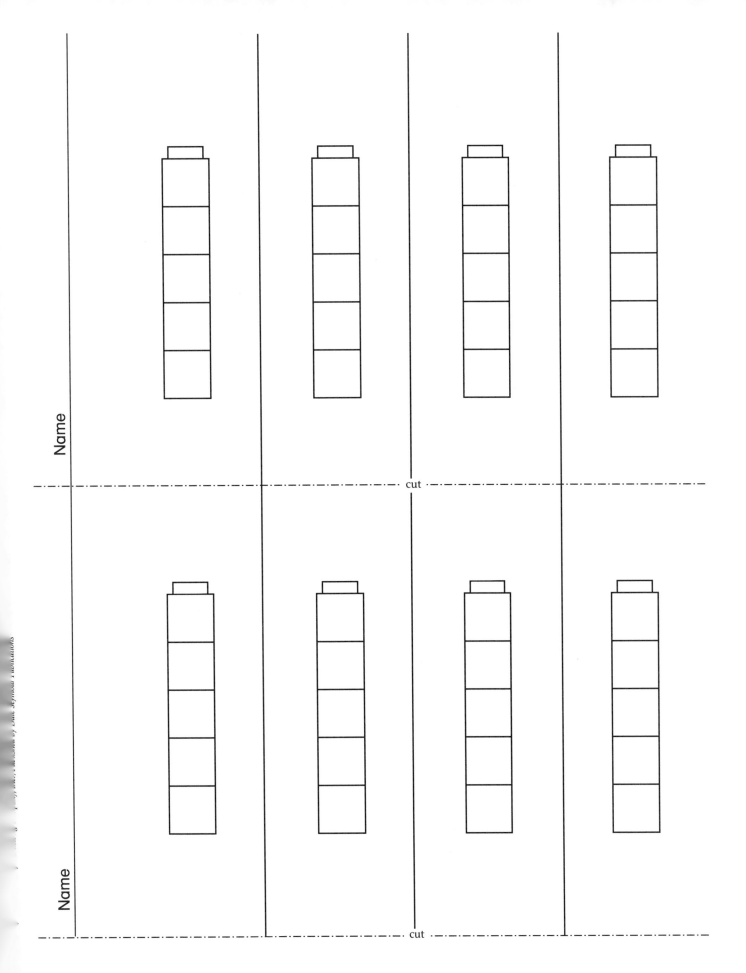

Name

Name

cut

cut

Number Trains Recording Sheet (5)   231

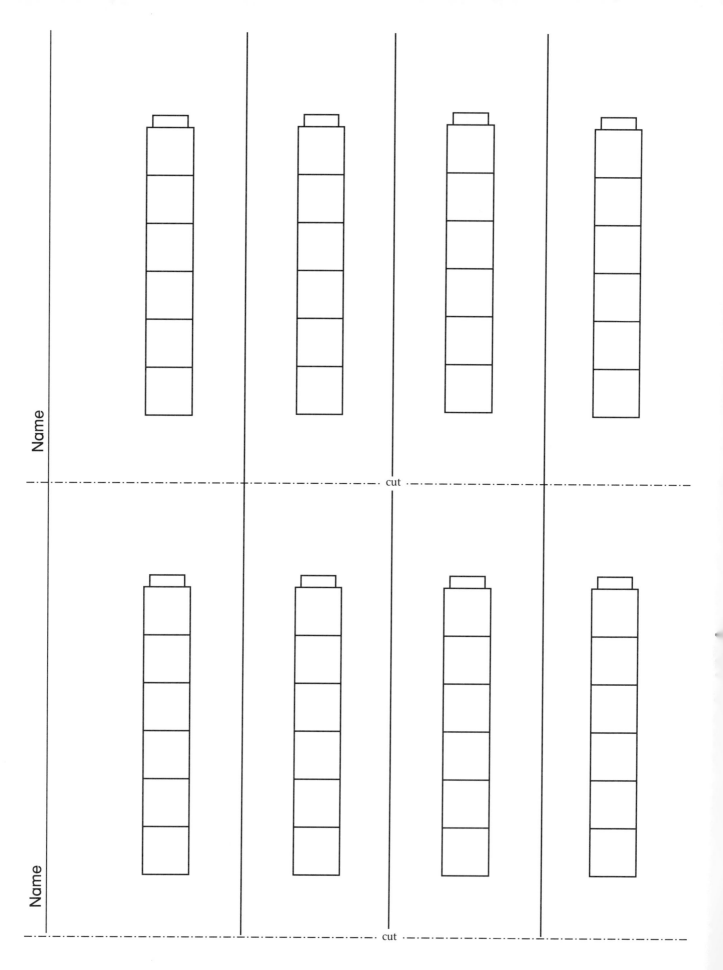

BLM 102 **Number Trains Recording Sheet (6)**

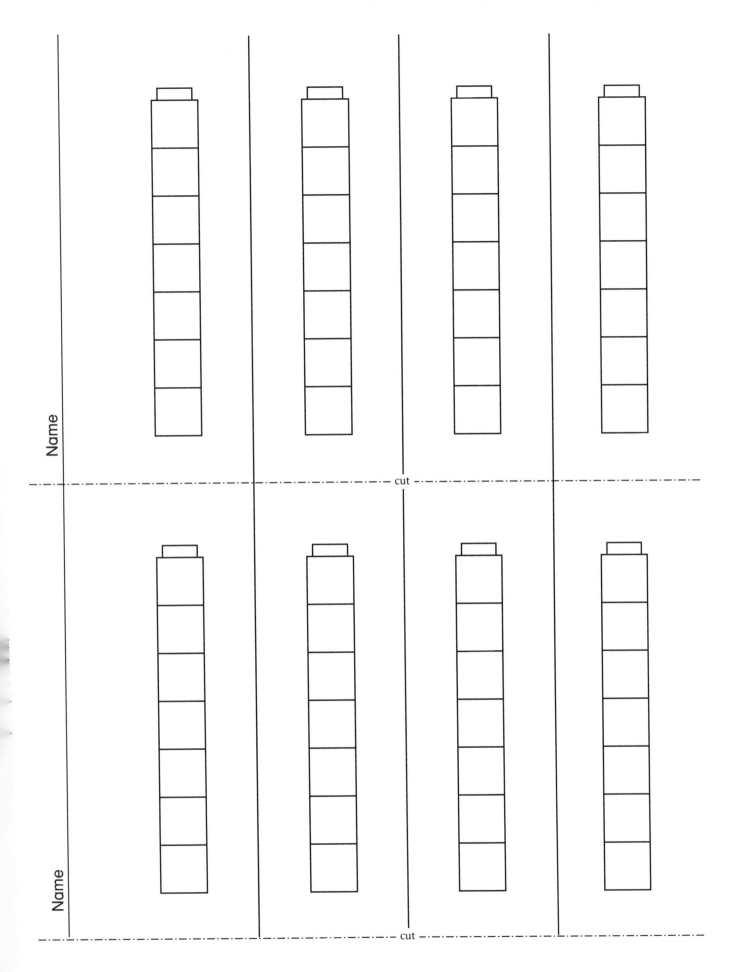

Name

Name

Number Trains Recording Sheet (7) **233**

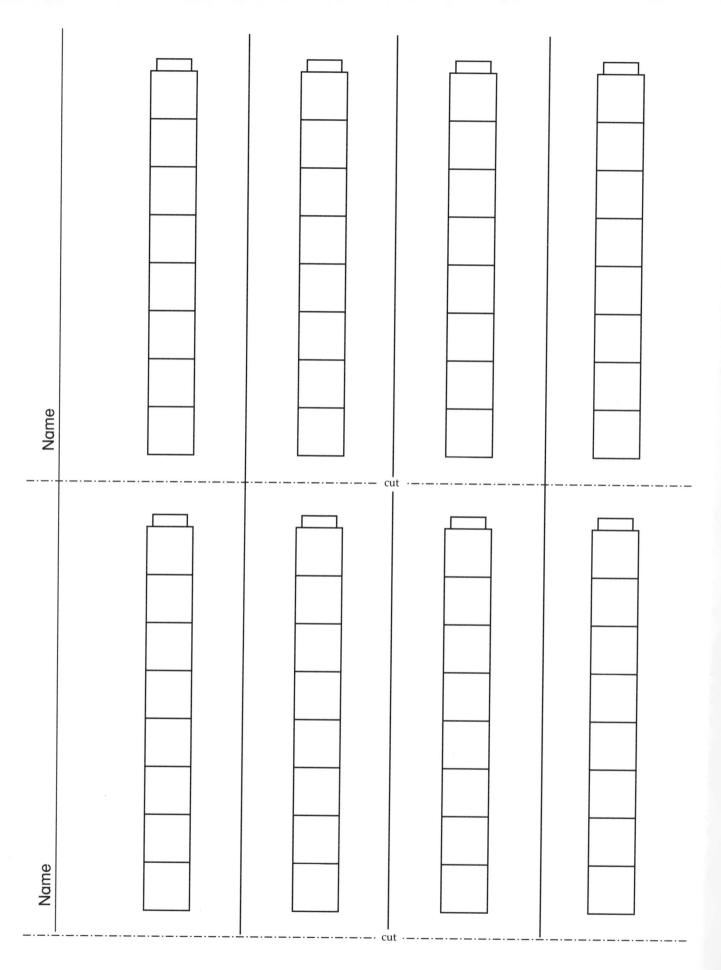

Name

Name

cut

cut

BLM 104   **Number Trains Recording Sheet (8)**

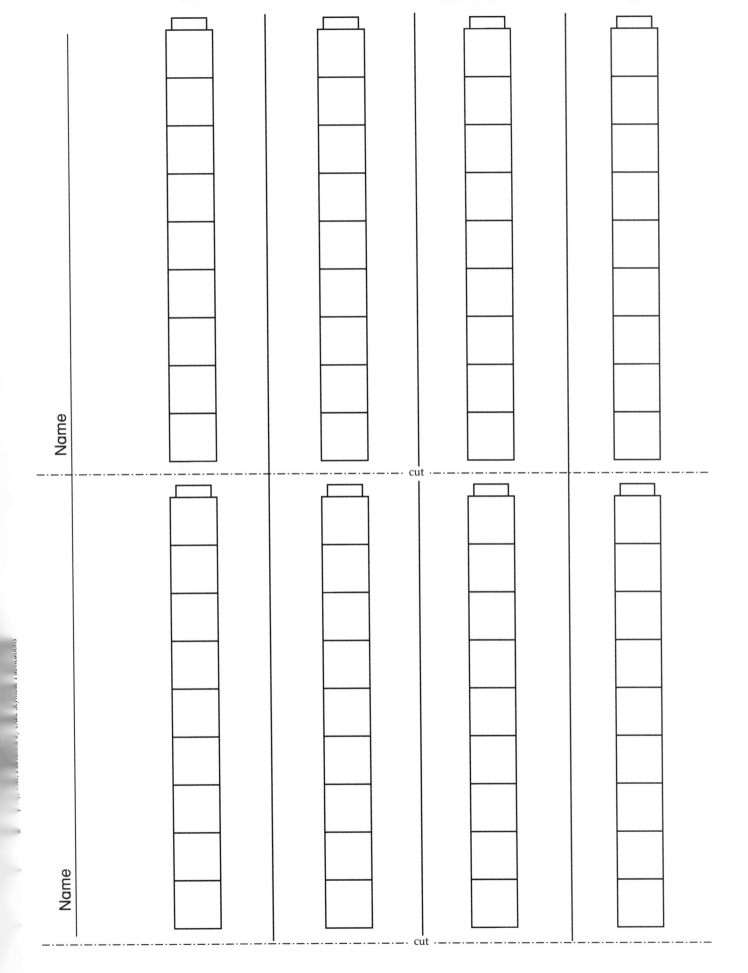

Name

Name

cut

cut

Number Trains Recording Sheet (9)   BLM 105   235

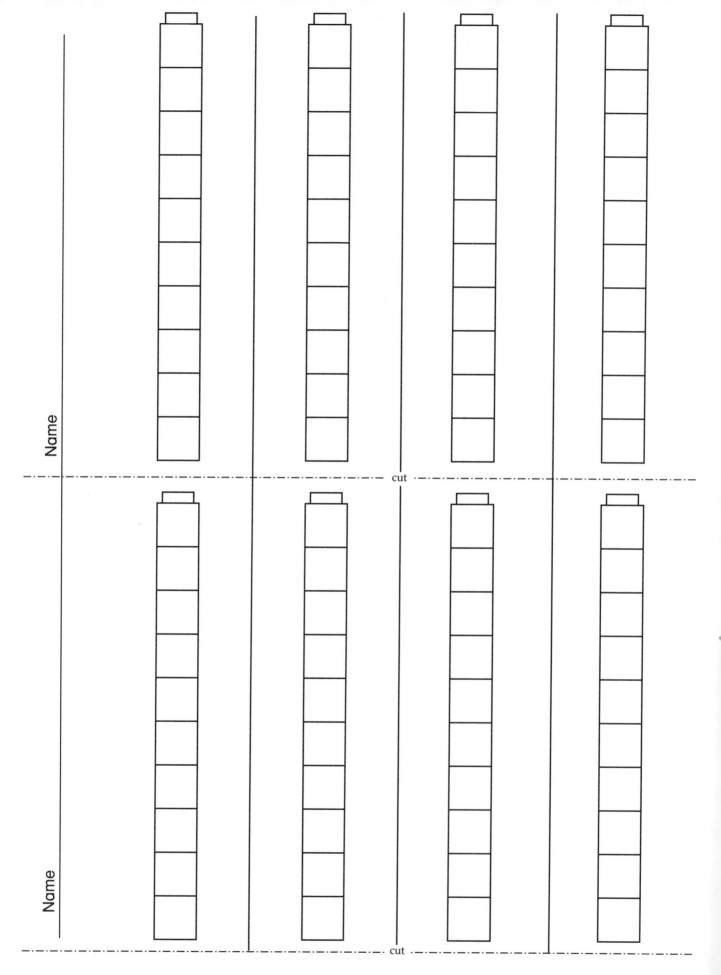

Name

Name

BLM 106 **Number Trains Recording Sheet (10)**

I worked with this number train.

I played a game today.
These are the equations I made.

BLM 108

Equations Worksheet

Build a Floor

- cut -

Build a Floor

Name

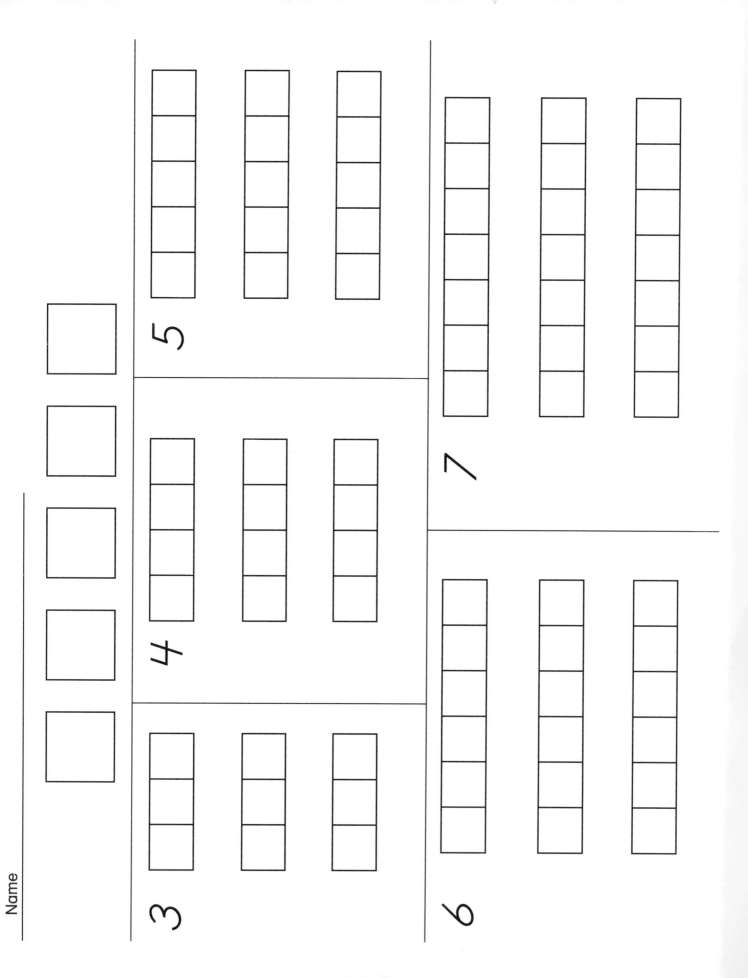

BLM 110   **Making Numbers Worksheet (3 to 7)**

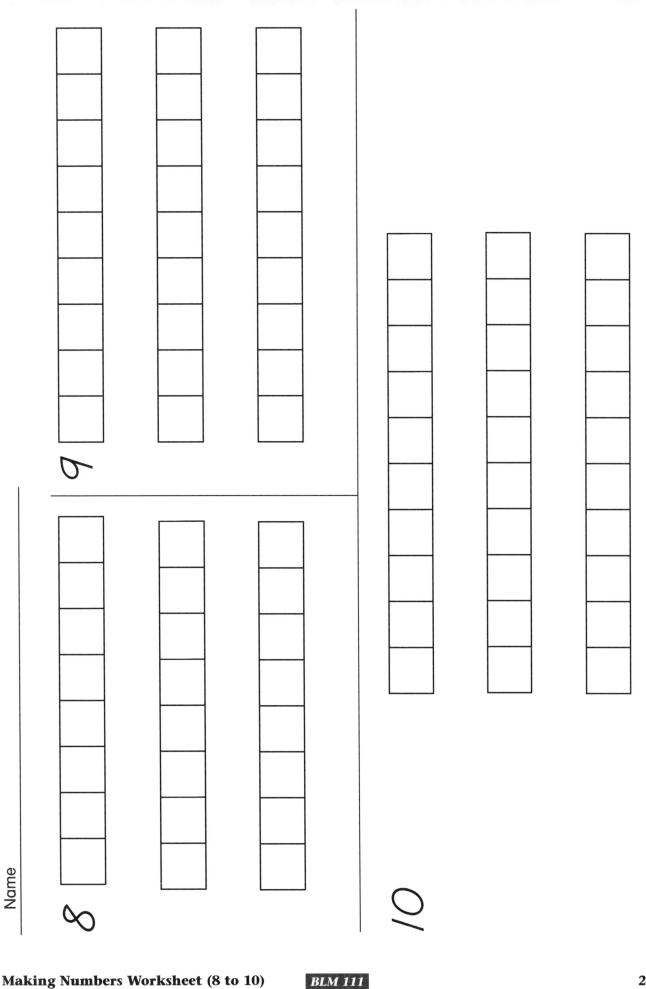

Making Numbers Worksheet (8 to 10)   BLM 111   241

- cut -

  Apartment Buildings Game Board

00	01	02	03	04	05	06	07	08	09
10	11	12	13	14	15	16	17	18	19
20	21	22	23	24	25	26	27	28	29
30	31	32	33	34	35	36	37	38	39
40	41	42	43	44	45	46	47	48	49
50	51	52	53	54	55	56	57	58	59
60	61	62	63	64	65	66	67	68	69
70	71	72	73	74	75	76	77	78	79
80	81	82	83	84	85	86	87	88	89
90	91	92	93	94	95	96	97	98	99

Professional Development Support for *Developing Number Concepts* Teachers

For information on the Mathematical Perspectives Courses and Workshops developed by Kathy Richardson to support the teaching approach in the *Developing Number Concepts* series and Planning Guide, contact:

Mathematical Perspectives
Kathy Richardson and Associates
P.O. Box 29418
Bellingham, WA 98228–9418
Phone: 360–715–2782
Fax: 360–715–2783